Give Stress a Rest

Top Trainers, Speakers, and Consultants Share Their Insights and Secrets for Dramatically Reducing Stress so You Can Enjoy Better Health, Confidence, and Relationships

Compiled by Doug Smart

James & Brookfield
J&B
Publishers

Give Stress a Rest

Managing Editor: Gayle Smart
Editor: Sara Kahan
Proofreader: Laura Johnson
Book Designer: Paula Chance
Copyright ©2001

Disclaimer: This book is a compilation of ideas from numerous experts who have each contributed a chapter. As such, the views expressed in each chapter are those of the authors and not necessarily the views of James & Brookfield Publishers.

For more information, contact:
James & Brookfield Publishers
P.O. Box 768024
Roswell, GA 30076
ℭ 770-587-9784

Library of Congress Catalog Number 2001093866

ISBN: 0-9712851-0-1

10 9 8 7 6 5 4 3 2 1

CONTENTS

Minding Your Body Under Stress

by Dr. Karen Wolfe

"Things are neither good nor bad,
but <u>thinking</u> makes them so."
— William Shakespeare

Are you often irritable, anxious and on edge? Do you often experience stomach aches, headaches or rapid heartbeats? These seemingly unrelated symptoms are among dozens which signal chronic stress, a problem that can creep up on all of us and can seriously damage our health if we don't do something about it.

Not all stress is bad. We can benefit from the stress of conditions over which we feel we have some or total control. The science of the mind/body connection helps us explain the ill effects on our body from the stress of conditions over which we feel we have little or no control. This science is called psychoneuroimmunology (PNI), and it tells us how our thoughts, emotions, and brain communicate directly with our immune and nervous systems and with the organs in our bodies. Every thought and every emotion has a physical equivalent in our body. So, be careful what you are thinking because your body is listening.

Stress — The Modern Epidemic

In 1990 the American Psychological Association reported that 43 percent of adults suffer adverse health effects from stress and 75 to 90 percent of all physician office visits are for stress-related complaints.

Prolonged anxiety and stress can result in burnout. Some signs of impending burnout include

- Working harder and accomplishing less
- Forgetfulness
- Increased irritability
- Physical complaints
- Increased susceptibility to colds
- Skin disorders
- Sleep disorders
- Increasing bouts of fatigue

Stress and Disease

The Ministry of Health in Japan has identified *karoshi* as the second leading cause of death in Japan. It is officially defined as a fatal mix of apoplexy, high blood pressure, and stress. Karoshi primarily affects middle managers in their forties and fifties who are characterized as being moretsu sha-in (fanatical workers) and yoi kigyo seshi (good corporate soldiers).

A review of the extensive research on the stress-disease link was published in the *Archives of Internal Medicine* in 1993 and noted a broad spectrum of effects:

- Compromised *immune function* to the point of speeding cancer metastasis
- *Increased vulnerability* to viral infections
- Exacerbated *atherosclerosis* and blood clotting
- Accelerated onset of *Type I diabetes* and the course of *Type II diabetes*
- Increased susceptibility to *asthma* attacks
- Ulceration of the *gastrointestinal tract*
- *Memory* changes

Because the medical toll of distress is so broad, relaxation techniques — which directly counter the physiological arousal of stress —

are being used clinically to ease the symptoms of a broad range of chronic illnesses such as:

- Cardiovascular disease
- Diabetes
- Arthritis
- Asthma
- Gastrointestinal disorders
- Chronic pain

Take this Stress Symptoms Test

How well do you manage stress? The symptom checklist below will tell you a great deal about the way you respond to stress. *Circle the number that most accurately describes how often you experience each of the following stress symptoms.*

	1=Rarely	*2=Sometimes*	*3=Often*
Your Physical Body			
1. Muscle tension	1	2	3
2. Headaches/neck pain	1	2	3
3. Grinding teeth	1	2	3
4. Indigestion	1	2	3
5. Chronic constipation/diarrhea	1	2	3
6. Rashes	1	2	3
7. Difficulty sleeping	1	2	3
8. Backaches	1	2	3
9. Physical weakness	1	2	3
Your Emotions			
10. Depression	1	2	3
11. Impatience	1	2	3
12. Loneliness	1	2	3
13. Boredom	1	2	3
14. Poor self-esteem	1	2	3

15. Resentfulness	1	2	3
16. Frustration	1	2	3
17. Overwhelmed	1	2	3
Your Actions			
18. Becoming hostile	1	2	3
19. Yelling/crying	1	2	3
20. Anger outbursts	1	2	3
21. Irritability	1	2	3
22. Inability to make decisions	1	2	3
23. Using alcohol/drugs/cigarettes	1	2	3
24. Eating more or less	1	2	3
25. No time for friends and family	1	2	3

If more than half of your responses in any of the three categories are 2's or 3's, there's a good chance that your symptoms, emotions, and/or actions are controlling you.

Recognizing your symptoms/warning signs is one of the most important steps in gaining control of stress.

The Mind/Body Connection

"Man's perceptions are not bounded
by organs of perception: he perceives far more
than sense (tho' ever so acute) can discover."
—William Blake

Stress is a perceived threat. Our emotions, attitudes and thoughts profoundly affect our bodies. Stress is not what actually happens to us but how we *think and feel about* what happens to us. Shakespeare was right; it is our *thinking* that determines our stress reaction. In long-term stress, which is perceived by the person as continued struggle or loss of control, the pituitary gland sets in motion a cascade of biochemical changes such as increased blood cholesterol, depletion of calcium from the bones, and reduced immune system functioning.

Ways of Thinking

To *"think"* is *"to imagine, to believe, to consider."* We have two main ways of thinking: rational and emotional. The rational mind is often called "left brain" and is rational, deliberate, analytical, logical, and linear. Alongside that is the emotional mind, often called the "right brain," that is impulsive, relational and sometimes illogical.

For the last five thousand years, Western society has believed that a linear, left-brained approach is superior. Only in recent years has there emerged a scientific model of the emotional mind that explains how so much of what we do can be *emotionally driven.* Because it takes the rational mind longer to register and respond than it does the emotional mind, the first "perception" of a stressor is *emotional, not rational.* Therefore, to really master our reaction to stress, we must turn to what is called emotional intelligence.

Emotional aptitudes are moving to the forefront of business skills as knowledge-based services and intellectual capital become more central to corporations and create the need for people to learn how to work together more effectively. For individuals to survive the strains of stress and for corporations to thrive in the face of change, we would do well to boost our collective *emotional intelligence.*

The Role of Emotional Intelligence

"It is with the heart that one sees rightly;
what is essential is invisible to the eye."
— Antoine De Saint-Exupery, *The Little Prince*

Intelligence is "the capacity to know." We have two main ways of knowing (two different kinds of intelligence): rational (IQ) and emotional (EQ). Much research shows that people with high emotional intelligence — *who know how to manage their own feelings well, and who can perceive and deal with other people's feelings* — are at an advantage in every sphere of life, including their ability to master the strain of stress.

Emotional intelligence refers to the crucial emotional competencies of

1. Knowing your own emotions
2. Managing your emotions
3. Self-motivation
4. Empathy
5. Social competence

All emotions are impulses to act. The root of the word *emotion* is *motere*, the Latin verb "to move," plus the prefix "e" to connote "move away," suggesting that a tendency to act is implicit in every emotion. For example,

- with *anger*, heart rate increases and adrenalin surges so you can take action
- with *fear* blood goes to the large skeletal muscles making it easier to flee
- with *happiness* comes an increased activity in the brain center that inhibits negative feelings and fosters an increase in available energy
- with *sadness* comes a drop in energy and enthusiasm which slows the body's metabolism so you can mourn a loss

Toxic Emotions

Evidence for the clinical importance of emotions has been mounting steadily. An analysis of results from 101 smaller studies into a single larger one of several thousand men and women found that people who experienced

- Chronic anxiety
- Long periods of sadness
- Unremitting tension
- Incessant hostility
- Relentless cynicism
- Suspiciousness
  Were found to *double* the risk of disease — including
- asthma

- arthritis
- headaches
- peptic ulcers
- heart disease

This order of magnitude makes distressing emotions as toxic a risk factor to our health as smoking or high cholesterol are for heart disease. There is a broad statistical link. It does not mean that everyone who has such chronic feelings will succumb to disease. It is helpful to take a more detailed look at the data for specific emotions, especially the *big three — anxiety, anger, and depression.*

Anger, Hostility, and Aggression

Chronic hostility and repeated episodes of anger put men at greatest risk for heart disease. The more deadly emotions in women may be anxiety and fear.

There is a large network of evidence emerging from dozens of studies pointing to the power of anger to damage the heart. The old idea has not held up that hurried, high-pressure Type-A personalities are at great risk for heart disease. But from that failed theory has emerged a new finding: *it is hostility that puts people at risk.*

Much of the research on hostility has come from the work of Dr. Redford Williams at Duke University. For example, Williams found that those physicians who had had the highest scores on a test of hostility while still in medical school were seven times as likely to have died by the age of fifty as were those with low hostility scores — being prone to anger was a stronger predictor of dying young than were other risk factors such as smoking, high blood pressure, and high cholesterol.

A Yale School of Medicine study by Lynda Powell of 929 men published in the October 1990 *Circulation*, showed strong links between anger and heart disease. The 929 men had survived heart attacks and were tracked for up to ten years. *Those who had been rated as easily roused to anger were up to three times more likely to die of cardiac arrest* than those who were more even-tempered. If they also had high cholesterol levels, the added risk from anger was five times higher.

A 1990 Stanford University Medical School study of 1,012 men and women who suffered from a first heart attack showed similar results. These were followed for up to eight years; those men who *were most aggressive and hostile* at the outset suffered the highest rate of second heart attacks.

An occasional display of hostility is not dangerous to health; the problem arises when hostility becomes so constant as to define as *antagonistic personal style* —

- Repeated feelings of mistrust
- Cynicism
- Chronic anger
- Bouts of temper and rage
- Propensity to snide comments and put-downs

Anger-Control Training

The good news is that chronic anger need not be a death sentence — hostility is a habit that can be changed. In 1990 one group of heart attack patients at Stanford University Medical School was enrolled in a program designed to help them soften the attitudes that gave them a short temper. This anger-control training resulted in a second-heart attack rate 44 percent lower than for those who had not tried to change their hostility.

Anger-control training teaches basic elements of emotional intelligence. Particularly

- Mindfulness of anger as it begins to stir
- The ability to regulate it once it has begun
- Empathy
- Thought stopping
- Thought substitution

Hot Reactors

Dr. Robert Elliott, in his book *From Stress to Strength*, refers to the concept of *hot reactors*. A hot reactor evokes dramatic and rapid increases in blood pressure as a result of stress. This ties in with the effects of anger on heart disease. The Yale researchers mentioned earlier point out that anger alone may not be the issue that heightens the risk of death from heart disease, but rather *the intense negative emotionality of any kind that regularly sends surges of stress hormones through the body.*

Depression — Silent Stress

These second millennium years could be called an Age of Melancholy, just as the twentieth century became an Age of Anxiety. Depression is a modern-day epidemic. Each successive generation worldwide since the beginning of the twentieth century has lived with a higher risk than their parents of suffering a major depression. For those born after 1955 the likelihood they will suffer a major depression at some point in life is, in many countries, three times or more greater than their grandparents. Childhood depression, once virtually unknown and/or unrecognized, is emerging as a fixture of modern life.

Depression is the primary cause of early retirement for men. Because men tend to be less comfortable in expressing feelings than women, depression may be masked with other behaviors, specifically, increased alcohol use, which may only result in a more depressed state.

Women are diagnosed with depression twice as often as men. This may be partly due to the fact that women are more open to disclosing their distress and partly because men often drown their depression in alcoholism, for which their rate is about twice that of women.

The October 20, 1993, editorial in the *Journal of the American Medical Association*, commenting on a report that depression increases fivefold the likelihood of dying after being treated for a heart attack, noted:

"The clear demonstration that psychological factors like depression and social isolation distinguish the coronary heart disease patients

at highest risk means it would be unethical not to start trying to treat these factors."

Asthma and Stress

Asthma has many triggers, and stress is one of them. Emotional stress triggers asthma attacks in both children and adults and makes the disease more difficult to manage. Asthmatic children suffering from anxiety or depression need higher doses of medication and spend more time in the hospital than other asthmatic children.

Dr. Wolfe's Top Ten
Emotional Intelligence Tips to Give Stress a Rest

1. Improve your ability to recognize and name your emotions.
2. Diversify your emotional portfolio and understand the unique role of each emotion.
3. Nothing eases stress more than exercise. Try to work out at least three times a week.
4. Practice anger management and frustration tolerance.
5. Recognize behaviors that may be covering depression, such as alcohol, cigarettes, drugs, and overwork.
6. Throw yourself into volunteer work, such as coaching Little League, being a Big Brother, or feeding the homeless. Service to others is a powerful mood changer.
7. Practice expressing your spirituality every day to connect with a power larger than yourself.
8. Laugh out loud — a lot!
9. Anticipate hot-button situations and prepare yourself.
10. Role-play troubling situations so you can try out some new self-control strategies.

Type-A Personality Revisited

In the 1960's, San Francisco cardiologists Drs. Meyer Friedman and Ray Rosenman identified a cluster of behavioral characteristics that seemed to be present in most of their patients with coronary disease.

These characteristics were

- *Constant hurriedness*
- *Free-floating hostility*
- *Intense competitiveness*

They coined the term Type-A to describe this behavior pattern; Type-B describes people who do not display these qualities.

Type A	Type B
Verbal and non-verbal impatience	Appears to be more relaxed
Hostility	Listens more intently
Fidgeting	Calm
Grimacing	Rarely, if ever, interrupts
Filling in during pauses in conversation	
Eye-blinking	
Sitting on the edge of the chair	
Finger tapping	

They undertook a prospective study to demonstrate that Type A behavior is a risk factor for heart disease. This was much like the famous long-term study in Framingham, Massachusetts. However, research since then has shown that the three aspects of Type A behavior — *hurriedness, competitiveness, and hostility* — were not equally harmful to the heart. Being competitive and getting things done quickly can have benefits. Hostility and anger, on the other hand, have little redeeming social or psychological value.

Fatigue, Sleep and Stress

Today we can claim with confidence that the single most important determinant of how *well we manage stress and perform* is where we are on the continuum from the high peak of optimal alertness to the deep trough of extreme drowsiness. The absence of this subject from most stress management and business leadership books is incomprehensible.

The scientific knowledge has been available for over two decades.

New research shows that sleep may be the third essential component of a long and healthy life, as important as a good diet and regular exercise. The more we learn about the science of sleep, the more we realize how the course of modern life has diverted us from our bodies' natural rhythms. In virtually all aspects of our life, we are overriding our biological clocks. When Edison invented the light bulb in 1897, people slept an average of 10 hours a night. Today, the average is 6.8 hours: from electric lights to all night television to split shifts at work. Before the invention of electric lights, our internal clocks kept us tied to the rhythms of nature. As diurnal (rather than nocturnal) animals, humans are not adapted to surviving in the dark.

Sleepless in America

Every week, Americans accumulate more than a billion hours of sleep debt. At least 50 percent of the American adult population is chronically sleep-deprived. Fatigue in the workplace is a bigger problem than we think. The National Safety Council's 1994 report on safety and health reported that the cost of accidents worldwide in which employee fatigue plays a part exceeds $80 billion a year. The National Commission on Sleep Disorders research estimates that, in the United States alone, businesses lose more than $150 billion a year in productivity as a result of employee fatigue.

In the final report of the Exxon Valdez oil tanker disaster, the National Transportation Safety Board found that sleep deprivation and sleep debt were direct causes of the accident. An even more dramatic tragedy was the explosion of the space shuttle *Challenger*. Not well known is the fact that the Human Factors Subcommittee attributed the error to severe sleep deprivation of the NASA managers.

The problem is becoming epidemic. The December 1998 issue of *Employee Benefit News* reported that 47 percent of employees admitted experiencing episodes of serious fatigue at work during the previous three months. Even employees who do not consider fatigue to be a problem can suffer from it.

It was not until 1996 that the American Medical Association began to recognize sleep medicine as a specialty. Before this, physicians looked for causes of fatigue in areas other than lack of sleep.

The Dangers of Sleep Debt

Within the vast knowledge about sleep, nothing is more important than the topic of *sleep debt*. If we can learn to understand sleep debt and manage it, we can improve our everyday life as well as avoid many injuries and premature deaths.

It is easy to tell if you have sleep debt. If you can lie down in the middle of the day and fall asleep in ten minutes, you have shortchanged yourself on sleep. Our level of daytime alertness is probably the number-one determinant of how we function mentally — learning, work performance and productivity, and our ability to manage change and stress.

Think of sleep debt as you do monetary debt — it must be paid back. Regardless of how rapidly it can be paid back, the important thing is that the size of the sleep debt and its dangerous effects are definitely directly related to the amount of lost sleep.

Sleeping for Productivity

Most of us want to be more productive. Many people feel they must get more work done by sleeping less. Our culture rewards the industrious person. Burning the midnight oil while finishing a project is very common in our culture. Could we get more done if we just buckled down and slept less?

During chronic sleep deprivation, performance deteriorates dramatically. All the scientific evidence points to the fact that every individual needs a specific amount of sleep. It is analogous to our body temperature set point. No matter how much our body temperature goes up or down during the day, it must average 98.6 degrees Fahrenheit when we are healthy. Getting less sleep over many nights only builds up the amount of sleep debt we are carrying. For a time we can pretend we are managing with less sleep, but eventually the sleep debt catches up to us.

Top Ten Sleep Stealers

1. **Stress** — Stress is considered by most sleep experts to be the number one cause of short-term sleeping difficulties.
2. **Poor Sleep Hygiene** — Good sleep hygiene is doing everything possible to foster a good sleep at night. This includes keeping a regular sleep schedule as well as avoiding caffeine before bedtime.
3. **Lifestyle** — Without realizing it, you may be doing things during the day or night that can work against a good night's sleep. These include exercising close to bedtime and working or doing other mentally intense activities right before or after getting into bed.
4. **Shift Work** — Shift work forces you to try to sleep when activities around you — and your own "biological rhythms"— signal you to be awake. Studies show that shift workers are two to five times more likely than employees with regular daytime hours to fall asleep on the job.
5. **Jet Lag** — When you travel across time zones, your biological rhythms get "out of sync."
6. **Environmental** — A distracting sleep environment, such as a room that is too hot or cold, too noisy or too brightly lit, can be a barrier to sound sleep.
7. **Physical Factors** — A number of physical problems can interfere with your ability to fall or stay asleep, such as arthritis and other conditions that cause pain.
8. **Cultural** — Prominent national leaders are sending Americans the wrong message about work and sleep. When President Clinton was running for office he publicly proclaimed that he went the last 48 hours of the campaign without sleep because he really wanted to become president. He was saying that, when you are trying to reach your goal, you can sacrifice sleep.
9. **Medications** — Certain medications such as decongestants,

steroids and some medications for high blood pressure, asthma, or depression can cause sleeping difficulties as a side effect.

10. **Television** — The number one bedtime activity in America is watching television. Move the TV out of the bedroom and you will remove a big sleep stealer.

Top Ten Sleep Tips

Below is listed a variety of methods for getting to sleep. They are all designed to help you deal with tension, stress, and anxiety, and to get a good night's sleep.

1. See a doctor — If you are having a sleep problem or feel sleepy during the day, a visit with your doctor is the best first step. Your doctor will want to determine whether there are any underlying problems that are contributing to or causing your sleep problems.

2. Establish a regular, relaxing bedtime routine that will allow you to unwind and send a "signal" to your brain that it is time to sleep. Avoiding exposure to bright light before bedtime and taking a warm bath may help.

3. Listen to music.

4. Avoid caffeine, alcohol, and tobacco in the late afternoon and evening. Caffeine and nicotine can delay your sleep, and alcohol may interrupt your sleep later in the night.

5. Sleep in a well-ventilated room and on a good firm bed.

6. Consider your sleep environment. Make it as pleasant, comfortable, dark, and quiet as you can.

7. Exercise regularly, but do so at least three hours before bedtime.

8. If you can't go to sleep after 30 minutes, don't stay in bed tossing and turning. Get up and involve yourself in a relaxing activity, such as listening to soothing music or reading, until you feel sleepy.

9. Keep regular bedtime hours.

10. Do not watch the news before going to bed.

The Bottom Line

Individual differences in the way people perceive and cope with stressful events is even more important than the stressors themselves in determining health or illness. The following are my top ten ways to start *Minding your Body under Stress.*

1. The only escape from stress, fear, and doubt is to confront them directly and see them for what they are. Retake the Symptoms of Stress quiz often to assess how stress is showing up in your body.
2. Learn to understand and express your emotions and develop your emotional intelligence.
3. Receive change with curiosity and openness rather than with fear and doubt.
4. Be sleep smart.
5. Exercise for at least twenty minutes a day, a minimum of three days a week.
6. Eat consciously. Allow your bodily needs to regulate your diet rather than being a slave to your immediate frame of mind.
7. Be conscious of your beliefs. Examine your beliefs and be aware of how strongly they can influence your perception of the world and of your health.
8. Practice mindfulness. Each day remember to do some activity with full attention.
9. Live with an attitude of gratitude.
10. Remember to BREATHE.

Recommended Reading

Dement, William. *The Promise of Sleep.* Random House, 2000.

Eliot, Robert S. *Is It Worth Dying For?* Bantam Books, 1984.

Eliot, Robert S. *From Stress to Strength.* Bantam Books, 1994.

Goleman, Daniel and Gurin, Joel. *Mind Body Medicine.* New York: Consumer Reports Books/St. Martin's Press, 1993.

Goleman, Daniel. *Emotional Intelligence: Why it can matter more than IQ.* Bantam Books, 1995.

Goleman, Daniel. *Working with Emotional Intelligence*. Bantam
    Books, 1998.
Williams, Redford. *The Trusting Heart*. NY: Times Books/Random
    House, 1989.

ABOUT
DR. KAREN WOLFE

*D*r. Karen Wolfe is an Australian-born physician, coach, international speaker, author and internationally recognized expert in the study of the mind-body connection and its relationship to stress and disease. *She has been speaking and consulting with clients such as Boeing, Rockwell, TRW, Chevron, Hughes Electronics, Marriott International and Mitsubishi Motors. She has authored seven books including* Medicine From the Inside Out, From Stress to Strength *and* Successful Aging.

Her practical approach and innovative insights provide corporations with a powerful format to improve employee performance in every area of their lives. She has a Bachelor of Medicine and Bachelor of Surgery. She undertook her graduate studies in psychology in California. She lives in southern California.

Contact Information:
Dr. Karen Wolfe
P.O. Box 3833
Mission Viejo, CA 92690
Phone/Fax: (949) 581-3269
E-mail: Info@DrKarenWolfe.com
Website: www.DrKarenWolfe.com

FROM STRESS TO SUCCESS — TRANSFORMING LIMITING BEHAVIORS INTO HEALTHY HABITS

by Natalie R. Manor

She leaned against the inside of her office door trying to catch her breath and stifling the deep sobs in the middle of her chest. Her head pounded and her ears were ringing like some incessant, irritating alarm. Her attempts to calm down were not working and she felt all resolve slowly leak out of her. Her office seemed small and crowded with paper and boxes. And where was her chair? She needed to sit down now! Finally her feet began to move toward the big picture window overlooking the main street of the city. The arm of the chair rubbed against her thigh and she slumped down into a smooth leather hug. Her breathing was better and the sobs were not quite as close. She rocked back and forth in her chair, comforting herself. She was unaware of the brilliant blue sky and enormous bright sun over the view of the city. Blankly she stared out, seeing nothing. The details of the previous few minutes became clear in her head, and she could not keep the sobs quiet any longer.

Stress. Huge amounts of stress.

Erika is not the type to cry about much and certainly not sob about anything. She is a senior partner in a prestigious law firm in a city rated as one of the best places in the U.S. to live and work. Her promotion one year before was a culmination of years of hard work. Probably harder work than most because her professionally learned behavior was not conducive to great planning, time management, and/or delegation. She was successful because she would spend as much time as it took to get the job done. And she had run out of time. There were just no more hours in the week or month to get the work done that needed to get done.

Erika is not untypical of many of us. How? She worked the situation through long hours and hard work rather than distinct skills and habits needed to successfully plan work such as:

- Time management
- Delegation
- Strategic planning
- Interpersonal skills
- Financial adeptness

Habitually Stressing Ourselves

As an executive coach, I deal with terrific people who habitually cause themselves enormous amounts of stress. And the stress comes from trying to do more work with less skill.

Five years ago most of my clients had secretaries, some administrative staff, no e-mail and at least 60 hours a week of work. Now they do not have secretaries or administrative staff dedicated to just them, work 80-plus hours per week and do have 200 e-mails per day.

The worst problem about the increased workload is not the time it takes to do the work. The worst problem about the increased workload is that my clients are doing the work with the same inadequate habits they had when they worked five years ago.

Time Management as a Skill

After 20-plus years working as a consultant, executive, and executive coach, I know that many managers and executives have little or no training in the exact skills they need to be successful. Take for example the process of creating a budget.

When I first became a manager with budget line responsibility in the corporate world, I was given no budget training. I learned how to do a budget by guess and by gosh, as my grandmother would say. I found old budgets of previous executives, asked my peer managers and found a book or two to read. But I was not given any training in how to do a budget. It was assumed that I knew how to participate in the budgeting process because I was now a manager.

Since it was assumed that I knew what I was doing, I certainly was not going to tell anyone I did not know how to budget. And you know what, all the managers that I asked in private about their budgeting knowledge admitted that they learned to budget by themselves. Some of them were very good at it because they enjoyed the numbers and had an affinity for the process. Some of them could not have budgeted their way out of a paper bag and they spent many hours agonizing over how to do their budgets.

I've asked dozens of managers and executives in many industries about this ineffective, stress-producing rite of passage to becoming a manager or executive, and all agree that it happened to them.

What about Delegation and Planning?

With the increase in workload and the shorter timeframes for getting the job done, the knowledge of how to delegate and plan seem to be dying skills. I've not met one new manager or executive in high tech that was given the space and time to learn or be taught how to plan effectively and to delegate tasks to others.

Management workloads have tripled in the last three years in most organizations I've come in contact with. And managers without good planning or delegation skills are spending more time trying to get the work done with little or no emphasis on learning the skills. There just does not seem to be any time to take time to learn the skills.

Interpersonal Relationships and Dealing with People

There is an organization in Boston that grew from 170 people in 1996 to 3,000 people in 2000. One year they had 1700 percent increase in growth. The turnover was 230 percent.

There were actually people in offices next to each other that had never met because of the speed of growth. And there were lots of people who did not know what the company was doing because its mission and vision changed so rapidly.

This company's number one issue for turnover was "ineffective managers dealing with people in an ineffective way" — the managers were unable to deal with the employees and interpersonal relationships because they had no time to deal with people.

So Where Did You Learn Your Skills?

My clients learned their most basic skills from their parents, teachers, friends, and family. Where did you learn yours?

We all start out somewhere learning our most basic skills of communicating. How did we clean our rooms as kids? Did we get our homework done? Were our parents compulsive, structured, good communicators, loyal, loving, efficient, effective? What about our early school experiences? Did we learn to plan, strategize, meet goals, communicate with bullies? Did we learn to read well, have great playground behavior?

What we learned and did not learn early on, and from whom we learned or did not learn, affects how we are today. Who modeled our behavior is very much where we are right now in our own adult behavior unless we have taken calculated steps to learn new skills and behaviors in a new way.

Cynthia — her mother was a compulsive cleaner of anything and everything. She dusted and vacuumed everyday. Nothing was ever allowed to be dirty. Every article had its place to be — nothing was ever out of place. Cynthia learned very early that she had better be exact or her world would not be a good and pleasant place.

David — his dad was a mathematical genius. He would pick up a math book and read it like the rest of us would read a great piece of fiction. The sciences and math were the only acceptable occupations. Everything else was inferior.

Elaine — learned very early that systems were how one should live. Each day and time had a meaning. Monday was cleaning. Tuesday was shopping. Ironing was done on Thursdays. Friday was getting ready for the weekend. Saturday was spent in the yard doing chores. Sunday night was planning for the week. Each day of the week had its own food. Money was only spent in cash — never any credit. And hand-me-downs were the first clothes you wore.

Cynthia learned to be rigid and things were only done her way. David learned that being a computer executive was his only career option. Elaine learned that someone else did the planning and creativity was not necessary.

And do you think Cynthia was good at delegating?

And do you think David was able to understand HR functions?

And do you think Elaine ever had much to say at the strategic planning meetings?

So What Does Any Of This Have To Do With Stress?

Cynthia, David and Elaine are high-level executives in prominent positions of authority working more hours than ever with higher levels of stress than anyone should be humanely working under. Their early-learned behaviors and habits are getting in the way of their being effective and efficient in ways that would better serve them and their companies.

Until the recent crunch of more responsibilities, more work and much less time in which to perform their duties occurred in the last five years, they were actually doing quite well in their jobs. Each one was able to correct any inequities in their skills by putting in more time. If a project was not going well, or needed additional assistance, they would just work longer hours.

Actually each one of us is able to hide some of our bad habits and behaviors even from ourselves because we can take the time to correct what needs to be corrected.

But we have all almost run out of *time*. And because we have run out of time and a place to hide our less-than-adequate habits and behaviors, we are exhibiting some very stressful physical and emotional side effects:

$#%&$*&%$#

80% of the workforce is experiencing stress

62% of us end the workday with neck pain

44% of us have stressed-out eyes

38% of us complain of hurting hands

43% use alcohol to cope with stress

76% of all companies have introduced new technology
*   in the past year*

The number of employees who call in sick due to stress has tripled in the past three years. Stress is estimated to cost industry $300 *billion* annually.

Coaching and Awareness Bring Stress Relief

In my career as an executive coach, I deal with marvelous people who are wonderfully talented in many areas. They can plan a new technology and deliver it on time and under budget. I've seen executives save mergers and acquisitions with brilliant negotiations that serve all sides of the business deal. There are managers and executives that can take their entire staff through change and growth and build loyalty that is the envy of their peers.

But the behaviors and habits that they have that do not serve them create physical and emotional stressors that create time bombs waiting to explode.

One executive who delivered the new technology on time and under budget had no interpersonal skills and when the project was done, so was his staff. Almost all of his staff quit when the project was completed. They could not stand his management style even though he was a brilliant technologist. This executive was so single minded about the project that he created failure by his own inept dealings with people. His behavior and habitual way of dealing with people was hopelessly unacceptable. And because of the time and money constraints of the technology project, he was not aware of how badly he was managing his people.

Elaine was the executive that led her organization through the challenges of huge change and growth. At the end of the process, the organization had systems in place that defined the organization and their work thoroughly. The organization and employees were able to achieve the growth and change in a rapid timeframe. All was well until the marketplace began to change and the organization needed to rebrand and become creative for its customers. Elaine was not able to understand the changing marketplace because of her habit and behavior of everything needing to have an exact system. Each system needing to be followed. And nothing substantial could be achieved without a system in place.

Under her leadership, the organization was not able to respond to the changing marketplace in a timely way. The situation was critical enough that Elaine was replaced with another manager able to take the organization through the rebranding process and creatively respond to the customers' needs.

You don't know what you don't know until you know it, ya know?

The incredible stressor of not enough time, added to the problem of embedded habits and behaviors, creates the perfect scenario for executive coaching. It is my experience that people can feel when they are not succeeding, and the best of the best seek help.

In dealing with incredibly talented managers and executives, I am allowed into their private professional world of work and all that they need to accomplish. When they hire me, they are looking for answers to difficult questions regarding why they are not as successful as they want to be or how to make something work better.

It is astounding the reactions they have once they find out that the "something amiss" is only habitual behavior that is no longer working: Trying to make systems work in situations where they are outmoded. Learning to delegate and to stop trying to control every aspect of every project. Learning to trust others with the work. Interpersonal coaching on how to deal with people and their day to day needs, wants and desires. Acquiring the skills of strategic planning and time management so that planning, not reacting, is the norm. Allowing people the space to be able to count on their planning and time management to make a project run more smoothly. Discovering that not knowing every aspect of every piece of the organization is ok — other people have talent and are allowed to use it and thrive in their knowledge.

Stressless Behavior — Stressless Habits

One of the best aspects of discovering you have too much stress is that you can do something about it. Our behavior and habits are just that — behavior and habits that are meant to be modified if we want. One of the best ways to find out if you are driving yourself into a stressful situation is to become aware of how you respond to change and how you plan your time.

- No one has to be in debt, overweight, procrastinate or create chaos. It is our habitual behavior that supports habits that are not working.
- Awareness of the problem is almost the entire cure. Once you become aware that you are creating excess stress in your life, you can make choices on how to deal with it.
- Action in making choices around new behavior feels great. Breaking a bad habit that leads to feeling less stressed and being proud of yourself is a wonderful success.
- Success breeds success. Once you create awareness of any habitual behaviors you don't like, take action around the habit to change it, and allow yourself to be successful at changing, you can repeat your successes more easily each time you make new choices around old habits.

Great Questions to Create Awareness and to Break Stressful Habits

Awareness of any situation is a great start to fixing or changing what it is that is not working well any longer. In executive coaching we have a process called the "inquiry" where we ask powerful questions in order to create powerful and revealing answers. By creating powerful and revealing answers, you are in a perfect place to begin to make significant changes in your patterns of habitual behavior — especially the habitual behaviors that are no longer working for you.

Take some time with these questions and see how they feel for you. What do they answer for you? What can you do with the information to allow yourself to be more successful than you already are?

Please ponder your answers over a period of time — maybe a week or two. Instead of looking for the one right answer, try using these questions as a mode of self-reflection, discovery and learning.

1. *What is working in my life and what is not?*
2. *What am I tolerating?*
3. *What seems to be the trouble?*
4. *What seems to be the main obstacle?*
5. *What is stopping me?*
6. *What keeps me going?*
7. *What is working for me?*
8. *What is present when I am at my best?*
9. *What changes in my behavior do I want to make?*
10. *What will my world look like when I've made the changes?*

As you begin to get the answers to your questions about your stressful and habitual behaviors, you can move to the next set of questions. These next questions will not only help you move from stressful behaviors that are not working, but will also build a new outlook for embedding really strong non-stressful habits that will work for you professionally and personally.

1. *What motivates me and what am I good at?*
2. *How do I choose to be this day, this week?*
3. *What is it to be a leader?*
4. *What powerful questions can I ask myself today to move me to a place that is powerful, resilient, resourceful and determined?*

5. *If I were at my best, what would I do right now?*
6. *What is it that I can do today to take very good care of myself?*
7. *What am I willing and unwilling to change and why?*

Stress is a Choice

Unrelenting stress in your life is a choice that many of us have made by our habitual behaviors that are not working for us, but working us. Being overtired, overworked, unappreciated, and out of sorts is not where most people thought they would be in their professional lives. Especially in light of the fact that they are working so hard, giving so much time, and, in many respects, getting less than the desired results.

Change, balance, stress, and success can be kissing cousins. Unrelenting stress, the kind of stress that creates illness and unbalance, is not an automatic that you have to accept any longer.

Success, balance, and stress-free living are achievable, but only through vigilance of what you want and who you are.

My coaching clients work each and every day to bring balance and less stress to their lives. It means a conscious awareness of the job, family, health, what is important in your life and how you want to live your life, and then taking actions to make sure that you follow through on what you want.

People go so far as to put a reminder to have fun in their appointment books. As we pursue our lives, any reminder at all is healthy. So put your stress-busting, success-building techniques in your appointment book, on the wall, in lipstick on the bathroom mirror — anything and anywhere that the reminder will help you break your stress-producing habitual behaviors.

My favorite writer, Ralph Waldo Emerson, has a poem that puts life in perspective for me. I hope it adds some food for thought to your life:

What is Success?

To laugh often and much;
To win the respect of intelligent people and the
affection of children;
To earn the appreciation of honest critics and
endure the betrayal of false friends;
To appreciate beauty;
To find the best in others;
To leave the world a bit better, whether by a healthy child,
a garden patch or a redeemed social condition;
To know even one life has breathed easier
because you have lived;
This is to have succeeded."

—Ralph Waldo Emerson

I want the best for you in all that you do. Many of us learned our least useful habits from the people who raised us and from valued teachers. We learned what we thought they were trying to teach us and formed these not-so-useful habits into our everyday behavior.

You do not have to spend one more minute with stressful habitual behaviors. You are allowed to have a stress-free life, be successful, and learn great new skills with ease. Life does not have to be quite so hard anymore.

Spend some time with the questions provided and find out the "new you" answers that will bring you stress-free living, successful new behaviors, and the ability to self-correct right now and in the future.

Please know that I send you my love and wish you a great life. Do get in touch with me if there is anything that I can do to help you find your successful new stress-free behaviors.

ABOUT
NATALIE MANOR

*N*atalie Manor brings clarity and leverage to her clients and audiences. She provides the means to develop extraordinary, high value
relationships — both personally and professionally — in order to become
superior performers. She is an executive coach, consultant, speaker and
co-author of Wholehearted Success. She offers powerful, practical and
on-target advice for mastering executive and team excellence, executive
skill building and communication. Natalie also instructs on corporate
workplace issues, with an emphasis on developing executive women.

Her KICKS audio tapes have been endorsed internationally in publi-
cations such as Entrepreneur, Self, Runners World, USA Today,
Kiplinger's, Prevention, Men's Health, and Paul Harvey's Report. She has
appeared on BBC's AllNight and on hundreds of radio and TV stations.
Natalie stays current with memberships in the National Speakers
Association, International Coaching Federation and American Society for
Training and Development.

Contact Information:
Natalie Manor
Natalie Manor Associates
P.O. Box 1508
Merrimack, NH 03054
Phone: (800) 666-2230
Fax: (603) 424-1267
E-mail: CoachNatalie@manorevents.mv.com
Website: www.NatalieManorAssociates.com

A "Wynning" Approach
to Finances:
Short-term Savvy Leads to
Building a Long-term Legacy

by Anja Wynne, M.A. and Frank Wynne, M.B.A.

O n April 1, 2001, twenty-four of America's finest military members were involved in an in-air collision with their EP-3E reconnaissance plane. The result was their capture in China and it was clearly not an April Fool's joke. I assure you the last thing on their minds was not whether they paid their April mortgage, made their car payment, or had a balance on their credit card, but rather on their safety and the state of the loved ones they left behind. It reminded me of a time ten years ago when the U.S. entered into a major armed conflict, the Gulf War.

The phone rang in the middle of the night; my German-based Army unit's posture changed and we were on a heightened state of readiness. The ground attack of Desert Storm began, and my fianceé, as well as the husband of the co-worker who called, were leading the VII Corps into Iraq. The radio commentator in New York could not maintain contact with Kuwait City, nor could the commentators for the Armed Forces Network television station, based in nearby Frankfurt, Germany. Our futures became a great unknown.

Much like those involved in the April 1 incident, finances were the furthest things from our minds. But as the ground conflict drew to an end and those forward deployed in the Middle East shifted into post-war activities, finances became more and more important. Family members left at home were responsible for maintaining long- and short-term budgets. For some, this was a new task to add to the daily duties of maintaining a job, keeping the children safe, explaining to them why their mother or father was not home yet, and serving as a liaison to the extended family. Many military families incurred unplanned expenses associated with traveling to their hometown for support, stress-induced spending sprees during the ground war, excessive spending upon the military member's return home, and ironically, for the lucky ones, astronomical phone bills. Unfortunately, many spent a great portion of their life savings, and, as a result, destroyed their marriages.

Stress affects virtually everyone at some time in his or her life, and it does not take a major military action to induce it. Faced with pressure, a challenge or danger, our body triggers the fight or flight mechanism, and we are able to react to dangerous situations quickly. Causes of stress are known as stressors and can be physical or emotional, internally or externally generated. Stressors can be events, situations, people or demands. There are numerous studies that attempt to identify the most common causes of stress. According to the American Institute of Stress, over the past two decades 43 percent of all adults suffer adverse health effects due to stress, and 75-90 percent of all visits to primary care physicians are for stress-related complaints or disorders. Stress is linked to all the leading causes of death, including heart disease, cancer, lung ailments, accidents, cirrhosis, and suicide. The impact of stress in the workplace is even more astounding. Job stress is estimated to cost U.S. Industry $300 billion annually, as assessed by absenteeism, diminished productivity, employee turnover, and direct medical, legal, and insurance fees.

Though there are countless opinions as to what the leading causes of stress are, there is a common trend. Money matters and dealing with personal finances generally tend to fall into the top five. Two of the surveys that support this are cited below.

Top 10 Causes of Stress

1) Death of spouse	58% — Conflicts with loved ones
2) Marriage/divorce	**55% — Money problems**
3) Marital separation	39% — Pace of modern life
4) **Personal finances**	39% — Working /raising a family
5) Death of a close family member	29% — Excessive noise
6) Major personal injury or illness	25% — Crime in the community
7) Imprisonment	22% — Violence on TV and movies
8) Unemployment	24% — Health problems
9) Marital reconciliation	19% — Commuting
10) Retirement	10% — Computers

From The American Institute of Stress on file at The Wynne Group

The State of Your Finances

Your average American single-income household will earn a fortune in their lifetime, and a phenomenal amount of money will pass through their hands. According to the 2000 Census the average American household earns $20,965 annually. Without investing a penny or accounting for raises, this family will bring in $796,670 during a 38-year career. Accordingly,

- $25,000 per year for 38 years equals $950,000
- $45,000 per year for 38 years equals $1.7 million
- $65,000 per year for 38 years equals $2.47 million

When you look at these figures, it is remarkable how much you will earn during your lifetime. However, the key is not how much you will earn, but how much you are willing to save and invest during this 38-year period. During the past fifteen years the national savings rate has plummeted approximately fifty percent. According to Juliet B. Schor's *The Overspent American: Upscaling, Downshifting, and The New Consumer*, only 55 percent of all American households are investing, and they average only 3.5 percent of their disposable income despite the expanding economy.

What is perhaps most striking is the extent to which Americans are willing to forfeit their savings opportunities in an attempt to upgrade their current lifestyle or "keep up with the Joneses." This is particularly prevalent in middle-class families who say they could save more but report they are unwilling to cut back on what one study calls "the new essentials." In fact, to finance their lifestyles, millions of families also send a second earner into the workplace, further compromising the balance between work and family time.

Unfortunately, approximately 25 percent to 30 percent of all households live paycheck to paycheck despite the second income. But they are well aware of the pressure they are placing on themselves and their family. A large number of middle-class Americans admit they spend more than they would like to, and more than they have. They also admit to losing track of how much they are spending. Simply put, many Americans cope with the everyday pressures of "keeping up with the Joneses" by overspending.

Luckily, not everyone is caught in this spending trap. Many Americans are recognizing the work schedules required to maintain this lifestyle are exhausting. These stressed-out people are wondering if the cycle of work is really worth it. Some conclude that it is not, so they start reducing their hours of work, lowering their income, and spending less money. These Americans are not willing to compromise their work/life balance any longer.

They find their jobs leave them drained and depressed, wondering about their function in life. Many realize they are spending most of their time at work, and that does not allow enough time for the things they really value. When they realize their life does not mirror their deepest values, they can successfully walk away from a high-power job in exchange for more meaningful work. They may not make as much money, but they are much happier. They are comfortable with a more leisurely schedule and a slower pace of life. They have time to spend on what they value, family and friends.

The most common trend of this segment of the population is they are making major work/life changes. They are finding career paths that complement their vision of who they are. Many are switching careers, while others are starting home-based businesses, working part-time, or leaving the work place to raise their children. Of course, finances become a concern and may require adjustments. Shopping is more limited, family gatherings become more creative, and a simpler lifestyle is rediscovered. For nearly all of them, these changes are worth it.

But is it possible to survive financially if your lifestyle corresponds with your values? Of course it is. You must set concrete goals, establish a consistent investment plan to support your goals, allow your money to make money for you, and enjoy the rewards.

Setting Concrete Goals

"Nothing happens, no forward steps are taken
until a goal is established."
—David J. Schwarz, *The Magic of Thinking Big*

It all seems so simple. Goal setting is engrained in our minds from the time we start school. But amazingly enough, very few people actually think through their long-term goals and even fewer commit them to paper. Over 50 years ago Harvard University conducted a study regarding goal setting. Upon graduation it was discovered that three percent of the class wrote down concrete goals outlining their future plans regarding career, finances, and personal aspirations. Thirty years later it was discovered that the three percent who wrote down their goals were more financially successful than the remaining 97 percent combined. The power of goal setting cannot be overlooked.

Many Americans have a dream of where they would like to be in twenty years. Unfortunately, it is often unrealistic, conjured up by movie images and magazines. But a dream can come to fruition if specific goals are attached to it. The goals must be clearly defined and, more importantly, written down. The first step is to divide your goals into three categories and estimate a dollar value for each. Long-term goals are those that you wish to attain in 15-20 years. Medium-term goals can be achieved in approximately five years, while short-term goals are realized within the next twelve months.

For instance, a long-term goal may be to provide a college education for your two children, which could cost approximately $100,000. Your medium-term goals may include paying off your credit card debt and traveling with your spouse to Europe for a summer vacation. The combined cost of these events is estimated to be $18,000. While your short-term goals may total $1,100 and be as mundane as getting the car repaired and replacing the lawnmower.

The second step is to make a commitment to your goals. Often we mistake being interested in something for being committed to its success. We tend to daydream, perhaps dabble in it, and then wonder why we have not accomplished the goal. You must be committed to do what it takes to create it and make it a part of your life. When we are committed, we will do whatever it takes — often turning obstacles into opportunities.

The third step is to review your goals on a regular basis. In much the same way many mistake their interest for commitment, many assume they are well on their way to achieving their goals. For instance, you may be estimating your medium-term goal of traveling to Europe will cost $5,000. However, prior to your departure you learn the cost of the vacation increased by approximately 10 percent and the dollar is not as strong when compared to European currency. By failing to review your goals, you did not account for the increase in the cost of travel. Reviewing your goals once or twice a year will allow you to adjust, add, or delete items from your list

Another wonderful reason for reviewing your goals regularly is the gratification you feel when you accomplish some of the tasks. We prepared our goal list the month before our wedding. After being married for five years and amending our list regularly, we looked back at that very first list and were pleasantly surprised. While we thought some of our goals were unrealistic at the time we wrote them, we did in fact attain 90 percent of them. Our goals included things such as having a child in 1996, completing our Masters degrees, and owning a home. After we revised our goals on our fifth anniversary, the day after our son was born, we added having another child in 2000. In early 2000 we reviewed our goals and realized we may not meet this one. Our daughter must have read the list too — she arrived on December 30!

According to Harold Moe's guide, *Make Your Paycheck Last*, financial goal setting can be summarized in six easy steps.

1. Start with your long-term goals.
2. Frequently refer to your list for encouragement.
3. Make sure your goals include everyone involved.
4. Adjust your goals as necessary.
5. Save your annual list to measure your progress.
6. The success of your financial plan depends on your commitment to your goals.

Establish A Consistent Investment Plan

After you establish a set of goals that you sincerely wish to achieve, you must commit to a savings plan that supports these goals. Regrettably, many families are so caught up in the daily cost of living that they honestly believe they cannot afford to invest. There is also a belief among some that if you cannot contribute 10 percent of your income, then it is not worth investing. This could not be further from the truth. There are many, many tools for investment. Some allow for monthly investments, some allow for one time or random deposits.

We are not the first to suggest you pay yourself first and certainly will not be the last. The reality is you earned the money and you owe it to yourself and your family to enjoy it. One method for insuring this occurs is to commit to investing automatically, and it has never been easier to do this. The beauty of this is that it alleviates the need for you to make a conscious effort to write a check to your account. It also eliminates the possibility of spending the money on an impulse buy and gives you the peace of mind that there will be money available if you experience a family emergency. Most importantly though, you can begin to really enjoy your life now instead of waiting until you retire.

A method for determining the amount of money to contribute to this automatic investment technique is to commit the total amount of your next raise. The rationale behind this is that prior to the raise you were surviving. You were paying your bills, putting food on the table, and keeping a roof over your head. While you have probably already spent this raise in your mind, challenge yourself to allow this money to grow for you, as you will see in the next section.

Money Making Money for You

One of the most incredible dynamics in finance is the power of compounding interest. It is almost magic to see how a sum of money can grow over time. If you put your money in an investment with a given rate of return and reinvest the earnings, the snowball effect can be astonishing over the long term. In this situation patience is truly a virtue. While it is sometimes tempting to cash out when the balance is high, be patient. Remember the long-term goals you have set and allow the money to continue to compound.

This chart provides two cases of how important it is to invest a small amount each year. For this example, both investors are committing $2000.00 a year and are earning a moderate 10 percent rate of return, which is lower than the average S&P 500's rate of return during the last 67 years. Investor A chose to start the account at the age of 22. In the first year the $2000.00 earned $200.00, which was added to the account, leaving $2200.00. During the following seven years, $2000.00 was added annually and the 10 percent earnings were reinvested. However, at age 30 Investor A was unable to continue to contribute. The account remained active and continued to earn 10 percent a year for 35 more years. By the time Investor A reached 65 years old, the account was worth $777,772. Investor A only put $16,000 into the account. That's quite a nice reward for remaining patient.

Investor B began investing at age 30, the same year Investor A stopped contributing. Investor B realized the same 10 percent rate of return, though had the means to contribute to the account consistently over the next 35 years. Interestingly, Investor B contributed a total of $72,000, considerably more than Investor A, yet the final earnings only reached $658,078. This is a sizable return as well, and of course patience again proves to be a virtue.

   While it is important to start early, it is never too late to start saving. Nor is it critical to deposit a large amount. As you can see on the chart, compounding produces modest yet steady gains over the first few years. But their consistent approach to saving netted both investors well over $100,000 before they turned 50. If you can commit to the moderate investment each year, and refrain from withdrawing funds from the account, the rewards are great. The long-term goal of supporting the college educations of two children can become a reality.

The Magic of Compounding

Investor A			Investor B		
Age	Investment	Total Value	Age	Investment	Total Value
22	$2,000	$2,200	22	0	0
23	$2,000	$4,620	23	0	0
24	$2,000	$7,282	24	0	0
25	$2,000	$10,210	25	0	0
26	$2,000	$13,431	26	0	0
27	$2,000	$16,974	27	0	0
28	$2,000	$20,871	28	0	0
29	$2,000	$25,158	29	0	0
30	0	$27,674	30	$2,000	$2,200
31	0	$30,442	31	$2,000	$4,620
32	0	$33,486	32	$2,000	$7,282
33	0	$36,834	33	$2,000	$10,210
34	0	$40,518	34	$2,000	$13,431
35	0	$44,570	35	$2,000	$16,974
36	0	$48,027	36	$2,000	$20,871
37	0	$53,929	37	$2,000	$25,158

Investor A			*Investor B*		
Age	*Investment*	*Total Value*	*Age*	*Investment*	*Total Value*
38	0	$59,322	38	$2,000	$29,874
39	0	$65,256	39	$2,000	$35,072
40	0	$71,780	40	$2,000	$40,768
41	0	$78,958	41	$2,000	$47,045
42	0	$86,854	42	$2,000	$53,949
43	0	$95,540	43	$2,000	$61,544
44	0	$105,094	44	$2,000	$69,899
45	0	$115,603	45	$2,000	$79,089
46	0	$127,163	46	$2,000	$89,198
47	0	$130,880	47	$2,000	$100,318
48	0	$153,868	48	$2,000	$112,550
49	0	$169,255	49	$2,000	$126,005
50	0	$188,180	50	$2,000	$140,805
51	0	$204,798	51	$2,000	$157,086
52	0	$226,278	52	$2,000	$174,094
53	0	$247,806	53	$2,000	$194,694
54	0	$272,586	54	$2,000	$216,363
55	0	$299,845	55	$2,000	$240,199
56	0	$329,830	56	$2,000	$266,419
57	0	$362,813	57	$2,000	$295,261
58	0	$399,094	58	$2,000	$326,988
59	0	$439,003	59	$2,000	$361,886
60	0	$482,904	60	$2,000	$400,275
61	0	$531,194	61	$2,000	$442,503
62	0	$584,314	62	$2,000	$488,953
63	0	$642,745	63	$2,000	$540,048
64	0	$707,020	64	$2,000	$596,253
65	0	$777,772	65	$2,000	$658,078

Invested $16,000		Earnings Above Investment $761,772	Invested $72,000		Earnings Above Investment $586,078

Enjoy Your Rewards

Ten years ago Desert Storm was an obvious stressor in our lives. In addition to the anxiety surrounding a major military conflict, my fianceé asked me to maintain his monthly bills. He entrusted his accounts to me, well aware of my nonchalant approach to money. Of course we both had automatic investments being withdrawn from our paychecks, but the hassles surrounding paying bills were still prevalent. Prior to his deployment he owned two cars and realized it was time to sell one of them. During the process of selling the car, his unit deployed. With a Power of Attorney in hand I agreed to sell the car for him.

I found a buyer for the car and proceeded to complete the transaction. The sale of the car netted $3,500. That was a small fortune in my eyes and a major contribution to a retirement fund in the eyes of my fianceé. Since his unit was not returning for many weeks, I felt quite comfortable using a portion of the money to purchase a beautiful Oriental rug and repaying his account over time.

We are now fast approaching our tenth wedding anniversary and cannot totally account for the balance of the $3,500. We often refer to the rug as our living room hatchback that seats the four of us quite comfortably. Some say he married me in exchange for the money, but we know better. We share the same values about money, family, and how to live life to the fullest. The Oriental rug is just another piece of the long-term legacy we plan to leave our children.

You have now established concrete, realistic goals; committed to an investment plan; and watched your money grow for you. It is time to relax and enjoy your success.

Balancing the various aspects of your life, work, relationships and leisure is critical to leading a happier, healthier life both at home and at work. Financial pressures continue to rank very high among stressors that affect individuals. Once you take control of your financial portfolio and the stress it induces, you will find that you are better prepared to maintain your personal work/life balance.

ABOUT
ANJA WYNNE, M.A.
AND FRANK WYNNE, M.B.A.

*F**rank and Anja Wynne are dedicated to providing Wynne-Wynne Solutions™ to organizations whose retention issues are affected by work/life balance.*

Anja specializes in cultural diversity and social issues that affect the workplace. Her military career, which has included living in many different countries, has provided her with a broad knowledge of cultural issues effecting men and women of varying nationalities. The NAACP recognized her accomplishments with the Roy Wilkins Service Award, an honor also bestowed upon General Colin Powell. She earned a B.A. in International Business and German at James Madison University and an M.A. in International Relations at Boston University. Additionally, Anja attended the Defense Equal Opportunity Institute, graduating with distinction.

Frank is passionate about teaching personal financial management to active duty military members and cadets, and is currently writing a book about strategies for investing while serving in the military. He is a Major in the U.S. Army on assignment with NATO. His military tours include Germany, Colorado, Texas, and the Middle East. He was awarded the Bronze Star for Valor during Operation Desert Storm. Frank earned a B.A. in Business Management at Saint Leo College, an M.B.A. from Regis University, and an M.A. in National Security and Strategic Studies from the United States Naval War College.

Contact Information:
Anja and Frank Wynne
Marlboro Road 9
41176 Moenchengladbach
Germany
E-mail: WynneGrp@aol.com
Website: www.WynneGroup.com

CHOOSING YOUR LIFE: STOP RESISTING, START ACCEPTING, BEGIN LIVING

by Paul Schnabel

U nless you are a turnip, a bedpost, or a broken record, each day brings with it new choices. Every fresh 24 hours comes with literally hundreds of choices that present themselves to us, choices that range from the simple (Should I eat Frosted Flakes or Bran Flakes this morning?) to the complex (Should I confront my abusive boss or let it go?).

Every day the world is asking you to make choices, and the quality of your life hangs in the balance. Will you choose to acknowledge current realities in order to change them? Will you choose to accept and love yourself unconditionally as a starting point for personal growth? Will you choose your life, with all its blemishes and imperfections, or will you choose escapism and fruitless fantasy?

What will you do? What will you *choose*?

Leading researchers agree that chronic stress and anxiety can be caused by a refusal to acknowledge current circumstances to avoid dealing with life as it is. In young children raised in abusive situations, the mind's distancing itself from reality is a key survival technique; however, as adults this practice can minimally produce anxiety and depression and, at its worst, can severely restrict our life's potential. Avoidance of reality makes real growth and productive change impossible.

And growth and change are what allow us to make greater contributions to our families, our organizations, and our world. There is no progress without growth — and our desire for growth, for expansion of our perspectives and capabilities, is both the opportunity and the adventure of the human condition. For you to desire a change in circumstances, in a career or in how you see and impact the world, growth is key to manifesting your destiny.

However, many of us never achieve what we desire. Many of us try something once, fail, and never try it again. Still more of us never even make it out of the starting gate! Others may achieve early successes, but are then sabotaged by old behavior and thought patterns that keep them stuck.

Does this sound familiar? Have you had similar experiences when you've set your sights on growth and change? Have you encountered such incredible stress and anxiety when you've stuck your big toe in the ocean of growth that you have settled for less, for a life that is comfortable on the outside but makes you melancholy and listless on the inside?

Then perhaps you have failed to choose your life.

Choosing your life! All those who have mastered the art of living understand what it means to choose your life. All of those who have reinvented themselves and created the life of their dreams understand the power in this concept.

I've heard it said that the definition of a true master is one who, if given the choice to change any past or present circumstances of his or her life, would choose exactly the life he or she has. Such a choice would be truly courageous indeed, for who would not wish to rewrite at least some aspects of the past or present? However, the power of this theoretical choice comes from acceptance of who, where, and why you are. By accepting your life and the choices you have made up to this point, you can gain the insight and freedom to choose differently in the future. Making new choices from that place of awareness allows you to create a life that will surprise and delight you, a life filled with passion and purpose instead of stress and frustration.

Many years ago I was going through a challenging period in my own life. My job was frustrating and unfulfilling, my finances were shaky at best, and I had just experienced the painful loss of a relationship. To relieve my stress and feel better, I sought refuge in external things — partying, big boy toys, junk food. These things would make me feel good for a short time, but soon the same old pain and frustration would return.

In the midst of my frustration I nurtured hopes for a better me — I thought of people whose characters and circumstances I aspired to and wished to emulate. But each time I tried to effect positive change I would find myself falling back into old behaviors and patterns. I felt like someone trying to rearrange the furniture in a darkened room, and I kept falling over the same chairs and tables over and over again.

I was what I now refer to as a "Try Baby." I would "try" effecting positive change for a while, but then I would encounter some resistance (setbacks, self-doubt, hopelessness) and would revert to my old ways.

Then at my lowest, most despairing point, I was given a gift of clarity. In one moment I realized that I was not facing my life on life's terms. I steadfastly refused to acknowledge or accept my current reality. I was living in a fantasy world of my own making that told me that *if only* other people would change I could be happy and stress free; *if only* I had received better breaks I would be successful; *if only* I had enough money I would be happy and all my problems would be solved.

In that sobering moment I saw myself and the circumstances of my life for what they were. With my blinders removed I was able to see things clearly for the first time. Eventually I was able to choose and accept who I was, where I was, and why I thought and behaved the way I did. By doing this, I was then and only then able to change those behaviors and circumstances, to make the shift from escapism to constructive action and change my life.

My friend, if I could do this, so can you.

So how can you start choosing your life? My experience, both personally and through working with others, has led me to see that there are three basic questions to reflect on in order to accept yourself as you are in order to move forward powerfully and constructively.

Who am I?

The first question to ask yourself is *Who am I?* A friend asked me this question many years ago and my first reaction was gut-splitting laughter. Ha! I know who I am! But when I stopped to think about it, I realized that I truly had no idea who I was.

As I reflected, I discovered that I was living with other people's conceptions of who I was. Much of my self-worth was based on how society judged my worth. My self-image was based on other people's conceptions of what I was capable of, what I was good and not good at. I had allowed others to build a box for me and I had gleefully climbed right in, pulling the lid tightly over my head.

Who are you? Truthfully answering this question requires courage, openness, and a willingness to shine a light into the darkened recesses of your mind. A truthful answer to this question requires you to think for yourself, which is not an easy task and is actively discouraged by many of the forces at work in the world today.

For every day we are bombarded by the "good opinion" of others, opinions which seek to mold and influence us. This bombardment occurs in obvious ways, as in commercials and political rhetoric, and in subtle ways, such as needing to dress, act, and believe a certain way to be accepted by the peer group of our choice, be it the kids at school or the other parents in the PTO.

Not only do we not fight this bombardment, but on the contrary, we welcome it, because it not only takes work to think for ourselves, but thinking for ourselves requires us to become responsible for our choices — responsibility that we would prefer to avoid.

The reality of our lives in an age of information overload requires that we leave some decision making and opinion rendering to others — our democratic society is based on that principle. However, when it comes to central questions such as *who am I* we need to go within, to the stillness of our being, in order to answer it, for perhaps the first time in our lives, for ourselves.

That is not to say that we shouldn't seek the opinion of those close to us in order for us to gain a fuller perspective on the question *who am I*. Sometimes we are not the best judges of ourselves, especially if we are prone to self-loathing at one extreme or grandiosity at the other. I have found that we are rarely as bad or incapable as we think at our worst, or as perfect or blemish-free as we think at our best. The truth is usually somewhere in the middle, and unbiased, loving observers can often help us see things in their proper light.

So, let's get back to the question. Still having trouble? Think about a time in your life when you were at your absolute best, when you were so engaged in what you were doing that hours went by like minutes, when you felt completely and totally alive. What were you feeling in those moments? Were you feeling joy and excitement? What feelings or experiences were you generating for others? Close your eyes and transport yourself back to that time and place until you are really there. After a few moments of remembering, open your eyes and write down what you experienced. This exercise will bring you closer to who you truly are. Notice that the focus of this exercise was less on what you were doing than who you were actually *being*.

Ten years ago I was a successful director of sales in a training and consulting company. But inside I was stressed and anxious, and I realized it was because I was not living up to my true purpose in life. I didn't even know what my purpose was, but I knew I wasn't living it. Around this time I signed up for a seminar designed to get us in touch with our life's purpose. Toward the end of the session I found myself writing the words "joyful healing" on my paper. I looked quizzically at what I'd just written. What the heck is "joyful healing"? But slowly and gradually the wisdom in those words revealed itself to me. I realized that I found peace and fulfillment by bringing joy and healing to others.

This insight enabled me to start living my life from that place, even in a career that most would not associate with being a joyful healer. As I lived my life in that manner I found new joy in my work and, not coincidentally, was more effective as well. My career took off. And more opportunities to demonstrate joyful healing presented themselves, both in and out of work. Eventually, by honoring this call, I ended up on my present path — as a speaker and author helping others follow their passion, live authentically, and embrace growth and change — and am fully engaged as a joyful healer.

Making the transition from a large company executive to a self-employed speaker and author was not an easy one. It required that I see myself and my capabilities in a new, expanded light in order to succeed. This realization was a primary motivation in my decision to leave my hometown of forty years and move my family across the country to a city where we knew not a soul, where we would need to make a fresh beginning. Why take such a radical step? For starters, this location offered more resources to me in my new career than where I was.

But more importantly, I found it necessary to start anew, with a clean slate, in order to more fully and quickly embrace my new self-concept. I could not make such a change while living where I had lived my whole life, reminded at every turn of who I was, not who I was now choosing to be. I also had to leave to avoid the phenomenon that challenges anyone who attempts a major transformation, to break out of the mold in some way. Colleagues and close associates will often say things like, "What do you mean you're going to be a (speaker, jazz musician, fill-in-the-blank)? That's a good one."

Anytime we embark on a journey of radical growth we upset the order of things in existing relationships. Some people are threatened because they believe you will start acting "snooty" and "better than." Others will secretly wish for you to give up on your dream so that you will return to the fold and assume your usual role and place in the pecking order. My decision to leave was the hardest thing I've done in my life, for I cherish many of my established relationships and eagerly anticipate our get-togethers. However, I know in my heart I made the right decision. For me, this move was absolutely essential to a successful transformation from who I was to who I am.

Does this mean you need to move to Timbuktu in order to effect major change? Absolutely not. But wherever you are, you need to create a support network that encourages your growth, in order to embrace who you are now choosing to be.

Where am I?

Once you decide who you are, the next question to ponder is *where am I*. Where are you?

OK, you're sitting down reading this book. Very good! But let's go a tad deeper, shall we? Where are you in terms of your career? What's working for you and what's not? Where are you in terms of your financial health? Do you have reasonable certainty that your financial plan will meet your needs now and in the future? Or are you just hoping that it will or, worse yet, avoiding the subject altogether?

Where are you in terms of your relationships? Do you have true friends in your life or mostly casual acquaintances? Have you learned the lessons from failed romances or are you still repeating the same mistakes over and over again?

Where are you in terms of personal happiness? Are you generally pleasant and content most of the time, or do you feel frazzled and stressed? If it's the latter, are you putting the blame on other people, places, and things, or do you recognize that the choice to be peaceful and whole lies within?

The greatest challenge to answering these questions truthfully is not ignorance but denial. Many of us refuse to see things as they really are, to face the truth honestly and courageously. It is much easier to avoid reality at all costs, to place blame on others and to engage in dreamy fantasies about how life should be. A friend once commented, only half in jest, as he raised a cold beer to his lips, that "reality is for people who can't handle booze."

Sadly, many of us settle for that kind of existence. An existence where we make ourselves feel good through alcohol, relationships, overwork, watching reruns of "Green Acres" . . . the list is endless. (OK, maybe not "Green Acres," but you get the point.)

In order to make better choices in our lives and change our circumstances, we need to acknowledge not only where we truly are in this moment, but also how we got here. Why are we where we are? Without this self-knowledge, any external choices we make are likely to cause a sense of *deja vu*, for we'll tend to repeat our past choices. Or, we'll take a wild stab in the dark at a new job or relationship without putting any real thought into it, leading to random and possibly even worse outcomes.

Some years ago a friend of mine was a salesperson for a large consumer goods company. His job was a struggle and he started blaming his company for his woes. "They're not putting enough money into research and development; our products are dated and overpriced," he lamented. He was placing the blame for his lack of success squarely on his company's shoulders, refusing to acknowledge his role in the matter.

Finally, a recruiter approached him about a sales position with a competitor. "This company is great!" he gushed. "They've got top notch products and have more coming down the pike. I won't have to sell with one hand tied behind my back anymore." He took the job.

Five months later, I heard a similar refrain. "Jeez, their compensation plan is terrible. I can't make any money here. Plus the operations people don't know anything about customer service. What a mess." Several months later, to his shock and surprise, he was fired.

Often it takes such a wake-up call to take an honest look at where we really are. His firing prompted deep reflection and soul searching on his part, and he realized that he was where he was because *he didn't like to sell*. He had ended up on a sales track out of college because those were the jobs he was offered by recruiters, not because he had a passion for it. This self-awareness allowed him the freedom to let go of where he was, to make new choices, and he chose to pursue a career as a corporate trainer. "I love being with people and sharing knowledge with them, but not in a selling capacity. This fits me to a tee." To this day he is a fully engaged, successful, and happy corporate trainer and consultant.

Why am I?

In his process of choosing his life, he discovered where he was in part by answering the question *why am I?* He understood why he ended up in a sales career, and that realization allowed him to accept that sales was not his chosen profession, giving him the freedom to choose more wisely.

Why are you in the career you're in? Why are you in certain relationships? Why do you believe the things you do or make the assumptions you make in your life? Do those beliefs and assumptions serve you or limit you?

Choosing your life means having full awareness of *why* you are *where* you are and understanding how your personality, your desires, and your fears have led you to the people, places, and things that comprise your life in this moment. Having awareness of these things is like shining a light in a darkened room; it allows you to see things you otherwise could not see and understand things that were previously a mystery. Now you no longer stumble and fall over the furniture, but by seeing it clearly you are able to rearrange it to your liking.

However, we must be careful not to use this knowledge as an excuse for remaining as we are. "Well, I'm just not a morning person, which is why I overslept and missed that job interview. I guess it just wasn't meant to be." Wrong answer! The correct response would be to take a look at why you continue this habit (oversleeping) when it consistently produces lousy outcomes in your life. What's in it for you? Avoidance of responsibility, giving in to laziness, and fear of success are possibilities.

Another key area to examine involves our assumptions. In order for us to make sense of our world we make assumptions, sometimes consciously, sometimes unconsciously. Making assumptions helps us function easily and efficiently; for instance, when you are driving and have the green light, you keep going because you assume that the drivers with the red light will stop. (Occasionally, this can be a faulty assumption.) We are not conscious when we make these types of assumptions; we just do it.

When it comes to situations that require more judgment, most of us process the present moment by filtering it through assumptions made in the past. The difficulty arises when we continue to operate from long held assumptions even when they are roadblocks to our growth and happiness. We get stuck when we continue to base decisions on assumptions that may no longer be valid, are limiting to us, or were never true to begin with. It naturally follows that if our assumptions are faulty or limiting, so will be our thoughts, actions, and, consequently, the results that we achieve.

What assumptions have you made about your life and circumstances? Do you assume that because you have always been lazy (bad with numbers, fearful, fill-in-the-blank) that you always will be? Or will you develop the willingness to see and do things differently? Armed with the self-knowledge of why you are where you are, it is then possible to develop strategies that will minimize or eliminate your weak spots and maximize your strengths.

OK, you've examined and accepted who you are, where you are, and why you are. What do I do now, you ask? Well, it's easier than you think. Start living!

Start living your life from a place of loving yourself unconditionally for the choices you've made to this point. You can't change the past, and beating yourself up for it only produces stress and guilt. Accept the choices you've made, and, if they no longer support you, make new choices.

Accept the outcomes your choices have produced, whether they have served you well or not. Denial or refusal to see the truth only causes depression and keeps you in the dark. Acceptance of what *is* brings with it a new peace and clarity and allows you to choose more wisely in the future.

Live your life based not on who you were or thought you were but on who you are now choosing to be. Your past does not have to become your future. Hear the beat of your own drummer, and march to no other. Trust that you have the power to create the life of your dreams, and then act and be from that place of power and certainty.

There were times after I started my own business when I doubted whether I'd made the right choice. I worried about finances, I fretted about my future, and I second-guessed the choices I had made. To overcome these fears, I took a step back and reconnected with who I was, why I was, and objectively looked at where I was in my life.

Through this process of honest self-appraisal and unconditional acceptance, I found the freedom and peace to stay the course, to remain true to my life's mission and purpose. But most importantly, I gained the strength and perspective to enjoy the journey and to surrender to the process of growing and evolving.

And in my best moments, if given the chance to rewrite the script of my life, I would joyfully choose the life I have. And that knowledge brings with it the greatest peace of all.

ABOUT
PAUL SCHNABEL

*P*aul Schnabel is President of Schnabel Impact Group, Inc. He is a *dynamic speaker and author whose thoughtful, humorous, and always powerful messages ignite the human spirit and provide actionable strategies for living our lives with impact. He has extensive experience in executive and sales management, team leadership, strategy design and execution and organizational change. He has delivered keynote addresses and workshops to a number of world class organizations, including the United States Marine Corps, Michelin North America, AchieveGlobal, Del Webb Corporation and Excite@Home.*

Some of Paul's most requested topics are: Everyday Heroes: Ordinary People, Extraordinary Lives *(personal power and impact);* The Journey of the Lamplighter *(leadership and life balance);* The Power of the Moment *(embracing change and risk, personal transformation).*

Paul is a warm and compelling speaker who walks the talk. His experiences provide powerful and inspirational examples to others about what is possible in our lives.

Contact Information:
Paul Schnabel
Schnabel Impact Group, Inc.
10875 N. 118th Way
Scottsdale, AZ 85259
Phone: (480) 767-8965
Fax: (480) 767-3578
E-mail: Paul@PaulSchnabel.com
Web: www.paulschnabel.com

CREATING A VISION OF GOOD HEALTH

by Nancy Hedrick, M.B.A.

Why do many of us take better care of our businesses than ourselves? I admit right away that I am personally guilty of this charge. But I have made great strides in changing my habits and priorities and would like to help others do the same, thereby avoiding the potentially harmful health consequences that often come with misplaced priorities.

When we focus excessively on the "health" of our businesses or careers, even under positive, motivating circumstances, we may be doing irreparable damage to our personal health. Any ill-balanced commitment may stealthily harm us physically, mentally, and spiritually.

Do we then have to sacrifice the health of our businesses to preserve our own? No. Certainly, there are times when we must put in extraordinary effort and focus, but most of us cannot go on like that on the continuous basis that our "24/7" world increasingly demands. Over the long term, we must prioritize our personal health ahead of the health of our businesses. After all, without good health, we won't be there for our businesses anyway, or more importantly, for our families.

In pondering the solution to this ever more urgent dilemma, I looked back in my career and reviewed the common themes of successful businesses. I wonder if in the pursuit of the long-term management of our health, we could apply what works in the long-term management of our businesses?

"Long-term" is the critical word here. We resort to many short-term fixes in business to shore up results, such as cost-cutting, price reductions, or new-product freezes. While meeting short-term business needs, however, these choices often have negative effects on long-term business health. So it is with our own health. Short-term fixes might include extra weekend sleep to "catch up," routine cold or stomach medicines to minimize symptoms, or caffeine to mask exhaustion. But while bolstering short-term energy needs, and alleviating everyday aches and pains, these choices routinely are poor choices for our long-term health.

Vision: The Cornerstone of a Healthy Business

One common theme of successful businesses is having a vision. In fact, I believe it is the cornerstone to the long-term health of a business. Having a vision does not guarantee success and sustainability, but it increases the odds dramatically. In my experience, having a vision led to three major results:

Having a vision provided the foundation for making decisions on businesses — We made decisions that best led our business toward our vision.

Having a vision fostered business management that was more proactive versus reactive — Our actions were based on advancing our vision.

Having a vision made for easier prioritizing — We prioritized according to what best supported our vision.

Why not create a personal vision as the cornerstone of our personal long-term health? It is easy to become stressed because of too many choices, activities, and alternatives. With a personal vision as our grounding, just like in business, we would find it much easier to make decisions, proactively take actions, and select priorities.

What are the characteristics of an effective business vision that we may apply to our health? I believe a vision must be *embraceable* and *timeless*, and have a *lifeline to reality*.

To illustrate, I would like to use Healthy Choice®, a brand I helped grow from 1992-1998, as an outstanding example of a business vision that contains these three characteristics.

Healthy Choice® was born because a man had a heart attack in 1984. That man was Mike Harper, chairman of ConAgra, Inc. Mike's doctor told him to eat healthier foods, foods with less sodium, fat, and cholesterol. The trouble was, when Mike went to the grocery store back then, he found no foods that met these combined health criteria that tasted anywhere close to good. Mike's vision was born: "Great-tasting foods that are healthy, too." How does this vision fit the three characteristics?

It is embraceable. To be embraceable, a vision must be memorable, understandable, and stir passion. How can an individual or team embrace a vision if they struggle to remember it, to explain it, and to be energized by it? "Great-tasting foods that are healthy, too" is simple, and as a team, we were easily self-motivated to help people lead healthier lives with enjoyable, nutritious foods. I can still hear Mike Harper's booming voice generating energy toward this vision.

It is timeless. To successfully drive long-term business health, a vision must be long term, too. The most effective business visions apply, no matter what market conditions exist, because they relate to timeless, fundamental human conditions. "Great-tasting foods that are healthy, too" is rooted in two enduring human conditions: wanting food that tastes good and wanting to feel good. With this timeless vision, we knew that the responsibility of our business team was to keep ahead of consumer trends in tastes and nutrition so that we could evolve the brand to meet those trends better than any other brand.

It has a lifeline to reality. There can be a fine line between vision and fantasy. To be successful, a vision must have a lifeline to reality. As chairman of one of the largest food companies in America, Mike Harper had the resources or "lifeline to reality" to pursue the vision. In just five years after its launch in 1988-1989, Healthy Choice® surpassed one billion dollars in sales across fourteen food categories!

Vision: The Cornerstone of a Healthy You

Let us now apply the reasoning that if a business vision is the cornerstone of long-term business health, a personal vision is the cornerstone of our long-term personal health. A personal vision also must be *embraceable* and *timeless* and have a *lifeline to reality* to provide you with the foundation for guiding decisions. With a personal vision we will still experience "stress," but it is now related to the excitement and natural anxiety of making the choices that best advance us toward our vision.

If you are thinking that you have never had a personal vision and that you are doing fine without one, try to remember back to when you were a youngster. As children we all had visions, though we did not know to call them that. Mine was to sing in the movies like Julie Andrews in *The Sound of Music* and *Mary Poppins*. Even if they were fantasies, nothing got in our way of imagining them coming true! Then as we grew up, we too often believed those who said that our dreams were silly and childish. As a result, we lost or dulled our vision. Without a vision, we lose sight of what we could be, focusing instead on what we are. Worse yet, we dwell on what we were.

I offered my insights on Healthy Choice® as an example of a successful business vision cornerstone. Now I would like to offer my insights from the evolution of my personal vision as a "case study" to help you with yours.

Case Study: Phase I
The Evolution of my Personal Vision to Help You with Yours

My first serious vision was to be a world-class tennis player. This vision met two of the three characteristics of an effective vision. It was *embraceable*. I could remember and understand it, and I was very passionate about it! It helped me make proactive choices. My college selection, class choices, and job decisions all supported my vision. It also had a *lifeline to reality*. Though not at the top, I was already competing at the national level in juniors and college. I thought if I could devote myself full time to tennis, I might have a shot. But my vision was lacking in one of the basic characteristics: it was not *timeless*. Right before my last year of college, I injured my back while scrambling for an overhead. My vision for a gloriously successful senior year and beyond disintegrated in an instant. Now where was I?

I determined that I needed to change my personal vision to one that was more endurable or *timeless*. I decided that my life's satisfaction would be to work hard and continue to develop the gifts with which I was blessed. No matter my situation or condition, I wanted to be able to look back and say, "I pursued my full potential and helped others do the same."

I am grateful that I learned this at an early age. Instead of pursuing "titles" and "promotions," which are not *timeless* visions, I kept focused on the businesses, and I believe I was much more successful because of that. In other words, the promotions and titles were the result, not the "end." Like anybody else, I had my share of personal and career disappointments, but in each case, as I remembered my vision, bouncing back and moving on were much easier.

My vision "to pursue my full potential and to help others do the same" served me well, or so I thought, for eighteen years. Overall, I achieved many successes and felt very fulfilled toward my vision. The vision was *timeless* and *embraceable*. It helped me make the choices that kept challenging me to grow and learn.

Contrary to a business vision, a personal vision has to be embraceable only to you, not to anyone else. Too often we fall into the trap of developing our personal vision — whether we formalize it or not — based on what others are pressuring us to be.

This pressure hit home when I was reading a study about why people eat healthy foods. The study reported two dominant groups and motivations. The first group's motivation to eat healthy foods was inner-directed. They did it for themselves. They took responsibility for leading healthy lives, and it made them feel good. The other group's motivation to eat healthy was outer-directed. They did it for others. They focused on how they appeared in physique, knowledge, and actions. Their ability to feel good was rooted in others' reactions.

When we are outer-directed, we put so much added stress on ourselves. In our society, outer-directed pressures keep sadly and ridiculously intensifying. How do we look? How do we dress? What is our title or profession? Have a vision that is yours. Have a vision that allows you to be who you are and not have to act a role others want you to be. Have a vision on which you can look back and feel good, a vision that is inner-directed.

The problem with my vision all those years, which I learned the hard way, was that it lacked a *lifeline to reality*. In my zeal to pursue my full potential, I failed to recognize the reality that I am human! I ignored the need to recharge, to take care of myself physically, mentally, and spiritually. I found this an especially difficult challenge in my younger years, when I was filled with the gusto of unlimited energy and the false security of its continuance forever. It is a challenge for all of us when we move into increasingly complex lives with both career and family demands, compounded by the accelerating pace of living and the distractions of our society.

In the pursuit of my vision, I asked successful people how they "did it." I heard many say that they had the right metabolism, that they had naturally high energy and needed little sleep. So I decided I did, too. I assumed their metabolism. That was an outer-directed decision that fostered my short-term success but ended up negatively impacting my long-term health. Succumbing to my metabolism fantasy, I convinced myself that I could get by on five to six hours of sleep during the week and catch up on the weekend. For my entire eighteen corporate career years I followed this routine. And rather than noticing anything off-balance, I actually felt good about my lifestyle management. When I became a mom, it was even more important to have time for family. So consistent with my old pattern, the simplest and seemingly most effective strategy for meeting business and family demands and "pursuing my full potential" was to cut back on sleep.

I turned forty on February 11, 1997. Friends and co-workers joked that once that happens, it is down hill from there. They weren't kidding!

It almost seemed like a switch was pulled. My energy suddenly diminished. What happened to my ability to catch up on sleep on the weekend and return Monday morning refreshed? Instead of listening to my body signals, I masked them as "getting older." Throughout the following spring, ongoing colds, swollen glands, and a heavy, almost paralyzing exhaustion were unshakable. When the "usual" remedies didn't work, I eventually succumbed and went to a doctor.

I feel very fortunate. My years of "pursuing my full potential" at my assumed metabolism did not result in a life-threatening diagnosis but a life-limiting diagnosis. The reason for my exhaustion was soon discovered — the Epstein Barr virus, which affects the immune system. With this news, I realized that although my vision was still *embraceable* and *timeless*, it needed to include the *lifeline to reality* of my own humanness and my health.

Defining and Creating a Personal Vision: Putting It All Together

After my diagnosis and doctor's orders to make a lifestyle change, I made the difficult decision to leave my corporate career. I used my recuperation time to revisit my vision. This was a wonderful opportunity to think about my gifts and interests and how I wanted to use them, and also to think about what was important to me so I could better prioritize health issues and manage stress. As a result of that hard earned self-reflection and study, I recommend an expanded personal vision that is not only *embraceable* and *timeless* and has a *lifeline to reality*, but incorporates our *gifts* and *what matters to us most*. Our vision goes well beyond our personal and professional goals. It is our "soul purpose," unique to each of us.

> *Your soul purpose is to pursue your gifts,*
> *aligned with what matters to you most*
> *in making a positive difference in your life.*

How do you create your own vision, your "soul purpose"? To start, take quiet, focused time or a personal retreat. You may think that sounds too "soft and mushy," or that you don't have time for it. Yet, this is often the approach taken in business before making major decisions. Management goes off-site to focus on the development of their business vision and strategic direction. It works well for business, and it will for individuals.

After developing your vision, I also propose that you annually review how you are fulfilling it. Is it helping to guide your decisions and thereby reducing stress? Does it need modification? Perhaps you have experienced a life-changing situation that will alter your vision entirely. In the business world, organizations review their business progress and direction frequently; so should we.

Why do we support successful processes in business and then scoff at the possible application to ourselves? It is probably for the same reason that, too often, we pay more attention to the health of our businesses than to our own. To get your attention, I am putting my recommendation to you in the form of a business memo, hoping you will be more likely to make a commitment if you think it is business related! Following the memo, I will continue my own personal vision "case study" to provide practical application of what the memo outlines.

Memorandum for a Vision of Good Health
To: The reader
From: Nancy Hedrick
Re: *Proposal to develop a personal vision of good health*

The purpose of this memo is to recommend that you develop and commit to a personal vision. Outlined below are the background, objectives, strategies, and key tactics. Also included are a recommended process, costs, and timing.

Background
Most of us are under increasing stress from the multiple demands of both our personal and professional lives. We want an effective way to handle stress over the long term. We want to increase our resilience to

setbacks, change, and conflict. We want to feel grounded and secure in our choices overall and in our daily lives.

Objectives

Develop a personal vision that:
- is effective for your long-term health
- provides you with a framework from which to make choices
- helps you manage stress

Strategies

Incorporate the following characteristics:
- embraceable (memorable, understandable and stirs a passion in you)
- timeless
- maintains a lifeline to reality — to your humanness — with a commitment to ongoing physical, mental, and spiritual good health

Add the following input:
- your gifts and talents
- prioritized listing of what is important to you

Key Tactics

- Devote focused, quiet time or a personal retreat to create a vision that is inner-directed
- Conduct annual reviews of your progress, degree of fulfill ment, and possible modifications

Recommended Process

Step 1: Affirm your gifts and talents
- Write down from your own self-analysis, as well as input from friends, family and co-workers, separate listings of:
  - your gifts and talents
  - your strengths
  - your interests

- Write down which ones bring particular joy and fulfillment
- Look back at your whole life; you may have left some talents and interests behind

Step 2: Define what is important to you
- Imagine you are at the twilight of your life in a wonderfully comfortable rocking chair. You feel a warm peace in your soul. As you imagine yourself looking back over the years, write down:
  — what mattered to you most
  — what you were most proud of
- You just won the multimillion dollar lottery; write down answers to the following questions:
  — What would you do with the money the rest of your life?
  — What would you do with the money if you had only six months to live?

Step 3: Determine where or how you want to make a
positive difference in your life
- Imagine you are at your ninetieth birthday party. Write down what the following groups of people would say regarding what they admired most about you and what positive differences you made?
  — family members
  — close friends
  — co-workers at different levels and functions
- Write down what you would say at your ninetieth birthday party regarding what positive differences you made in all aspects of your life?

Step 4: Put it all together
- Reflect upon and review all the information you have written down during the previous three steps and organize it into your "soul purpose" as suggested below:

— What are your gifts that you want to be a part of your vision? Pick 3-5 of the gifts listed in Step 1. (A vision using your gifts will provide you with more success and fulfillment due to the natural energy, joy, and confidence that results when utilizing them.)

— What matters to you most? Pick 4-6 from the list generated in Step 2, and prioritize them. (A prioritization of what matters to you most will help in decision making when you seem overwhelmed with possibilities and alternatives.)

— What positive differences do you want to make in your life? Review your responses to Step 3.

- Review again your collective responses for additions, modifications, and confirmation

- Write down your final version of your "soul purpose":
  Your soul purpose is to pursue your gifts
  (insert your list of gifts}
  aligned with what matters to you most
  (insert your prioritized list)
  in making a positive difference.
  (describe)

Cost: Priceless, invaluable

Opportunity cost of not proceeding: Your long-term physical, mental, and spiritual health

Timing: Start now!

My Case Study:
Phase II — Continued Application

As best I can, I use the following as my personal vision for direction, decisions, and long-term health management. It was created using the process outlined in the memo. You may have other ideas and approaches to help you to arrive at your own vision.

My soul purpose is to pursue my gifts:
— *the ability to see, sense, and connect*

— *the ability to lead, motivate, and inspire*
— *resilience and inner-strength*
aligned with what matters to me most
1. God
2. Honesty and integrity
3. Health (mental, physical, spiritual)
4. Family
5. Career
in making a positive difference
by regenerating personal courage and initiative in myself and
others to pursue their full potential.

You can see that my soul purpose evolved out of where I was with the vision "to pursue my full potential and help others do the same." This vision is *embraceable* to me, *timeless*, and includes the *lifeline to reality* of my humanness. By adding my *gifts* and *what is important to me*, I have a more complete and helpful framework from which to guide my life and manage stress.

By including *my gifts*, I am much more conscious of using and further developing them, which brings tremendous fulfillment. Not every part of your personal and professional life will use all your gifts, but you can plan to use them collectively across different endeavors — for example, my desire to help lead children to pursue their potential was fulfilled through my volunteer time with two different children's charities — or sequenced through life — for the first time, I am pursuing writing and taking singing lessons (look out, Julie Andrews!) as new approaches in expanding my gift to lead, motivate, and inspire.

Similarly, a prioritized list of *what is important to me* helps me make better decisions with less stress. For example, I now put health ahead of my family and career because I have learned that without your heath you are not there for your family or career anyway. It used to be so easy for me to put those demands ahead of my own health. Now that I have it written into my vision, I am better at saying "no" when I begin to feel that family or career demands are starting to affect my health again. Currently, I have family prioritized ahead of my career. This is also intentional, given that I have children in the critical teenage years. In my "look-back exercise," I realized that I did not want to miss being there for them during these tough growing-up years. On the other hand, there may be times when you decide that your career comes before family, such as after an important promotion opportunity or going back to school. The key to minimizing stress is to gain family support for your prioritization and agreement to the time frame.

I admit that it isn't always easy to stay focused on your vision. But it provides you with an anchor and a sense of purpose so that you never feel stranded, lost, or afloat. And there is the risk that it may never be achieved. But often the joy is in the journey. Who knows if I will ever reach my full potential, but I am going to have a fun and fulfilling life trying.

After I left the corporate world due to health, many people said, "God must have been telling you to slow down." I thought perhaps it was true that God was sending me a message.

Then I realized that I couldn't blame God or anyone else. I lost my good health because of the unhealthy choices I had made. I must take responsibility for that.

Take responsibility for your own long-term health, physically, mentally, and spiritually by making choices that are healthy. Start by creating and committing to a personal vision, your "soul purpose": one that is *embraceable* and *timeless*, one that includes your *gifts* and *what matters to you most*— most importantly, one with a *lifeline to reality* to your individual humanness. Put your long-term health ahead of the long-term health of your business. Be a vision of good health.

Healthy Choice® is a registered trademark of ConAgra Brands, Inc., and is used with permission from ConAgra Foods, Inc.

ABOUT
NANCY HEDRICK, M.B.A.

*N*ancy Hedrick is president of ReGen Enterprises, LLC, a company she founded in 1999. Nancy works with organizations that want to foster and regenerate the personal courage and initiative of each employee to pursue their full potential so that they can contribute with greater positive impact to the overall success of the company. Through ReGen Enterprises, Nancy's focus is consulting in the areas of strategic planning and positioning as well as professional speaking through keynotes and workshops in communication, resilience and leadership.

Nancy's approach is grounded in eighteen successful years in consumer marketing and corporate management. In her ten years at General Mills, Nancy led the brands Pop Secret®, Gold Medal® Flour, Bisquick®, and several brands from Betty Crocker® and General Mills cereals. She then worked for seven years with ConAgra Frozen Foods where she became senior vice president of marketing, managing close to $2 billion in retail dollar sales of brands that included Healthy Choice®, Marie Callenders®, and Banquet® Nancy and her teams won many company and industry awards in marketing and advertising. Nancy has also applied her principles of success as a national-level tennis player and collegiate coach.

Contact Information:
Nancy Hedrick
ReGen Enterprises, LLC
12811 West 131st Street
Overland Park, KS 66213
Phone: (913) 814-9504
Fax: (913) 685-7413
E-mail: nchedrick@aol.com
Website: www.ReGen-Ent.com

STRESS!
MINE AND YOURS:
Do We Stress Ourselves and Each Other?

by Gerry Grinold

"**W**ould you like to move stress away from you?" As an international personal development trainer, that is a question I often ask my audiences. Whether I'm in Aberdeen, Scotland; London, England; New York City or Sioux City, Iowa, the resounding, confirming response is always — YES! Yes, I do want to move stress away from me and get a life. We all have 168 hours a week to live our lives, so why do some people have a life while others are trying to find theirs? The answer lies in the ability to control one's level of stress. Some stress is good — even healthy for us. Getting out of our comfort zone and trying new techniques is a healthy stretch, and in the long run reduces the stress factor.

Remember your first job interview? Mine was for a waitress position at a Big Boy Restaurant. My mind was reeling with questions like: "Will I get the job?" "What should I say?" "What are they going to ask me?" It was all I could do to get out of the car and take those first steps to meet the manager. How common it is to be fearful on the inside, trying not to show it on our face or in our voice. But there it is. The stress of it all. Uncomfortable? You bet. We would rather be doing anything other than what makes us feel fearful and uncomfortable. But guess what? Confidence is gained and stress lessened each time we conquer new and uncomfortable events in our lives.

It's easy to say, "I want to have less stress. I want to handle this situation more effectively. I want to build better relationships and have a more comfortable life." It's more difficult to actually accomplish these goals. Successfully moving stress away from you will require a deep commitment to the following three steps:

Step 1. A Heartfelt Need

Step 2. New Skills and Knowledge

Step 3. Action

Step 1. A Heartfelt Need

We can talk about the benefits of managing stress, communicating more effectively, and controlling our emotions, but just acknowledging these rewards is not enough. Almost everyone acknowledges the benefits of eating healthy foods, exercising daily, and not smoking, but it takes a personal, heartfelt need to make any changes. The same is true about giving stress a rest — or moving it away from us. We have to accept the responsibility, take ownership, and really want to make some changes, or we will continue to have the same stress levels. You know people who say, "I'm so stressed." "My life is so hectic." "That really irritates me." Do you know them, or are you one of them? Did you see or hear yourself?

Stan wants to make absolutely sure he has the most up-to-date facts before making a decision. He says to Margaret, "I think we need to research this in more detail before we present it to the board of directors. I know of three excellent web sites that could give us a .0683 percent slant on all the figures and graphs we are currently working on." Margaret is about ready to pull her lip up over her eyebrows with impatience. She feels they have the bullet-point facts, should present them now, and move forward to the next project. Talk about *stress*: Stan's detailed, controlling stress; Margaret's anxious, on-edge stress. Their opposite points of view, different needs and objectives, and contrasting ways of getting results needlessly cause a strain on the relationship and a gap in their communication.

In Dr. Steven Covey's book, *The Seven Habits of Highly Effective People*, he gives us Habit #5, which is so powerful. *"Seek first to understand, then to be understood."* All of us have a natural human need to be understood. If we are going to put Habit #5 into action, we must recognize the importance of trying first to understand others before expecting them to understand us. That is why this habit is so very difficult to accomplish, yet so powerful in reducing our stress. If Stan would try to understand Margaret's intentions, and Margaret would try to be a little more flexible with Stan's attention to details, it would eliminate some of the stress. We do cause stress to ourselves and to each other.

Step 2. New Skills and Knowledge

I was presenting an "Improving Your Communication Skills" Seminar on Long Island. I had an elbow-to-elbow situation with approximately 120 attendees. There was a gentleman sitting in the front row wearing a yellow baseball cap, attentively absorbing the information presented. He was participating in discussions and had a positive aura about him. At the first break, I welcomed the opportunity to meet him. I introduced myself and thanked him for sitting in the front row. (Speakers love front row people.) I asked Herbert, "What brought you to this seminar? What do you want to get out of the day?" Herbert gave me a warm, friendly smile and responded, "Well, I've had a couple successful careers over my life and I'm always open to seeing what else I can learn, what new skills I can acquire." He proceeded to tell me that he was 90 years young and that he just wanted to be a better communicator.

Herbert gave me permission to introduce him to the audience and share his age. At the close of the seminar I had him stand beside me at the front of the room. I told the audience that Herbert had attended today's seminar because he truly wanted to learn some new skills and become an even better communicator at 90 years of age. That audience spontaneously gave Herbert the most jubilant standing ovation. Herbert turned sideways, briskly pulled his yellow baseball cap off his head, and waved it in the air as if he had just won the Indianapolis 500. What an inspiration Herbert was to all of us!

By continuing to be open to learning new skills and gaining valuable knowledge, Herbert has given himself some additional tools to give stress a rest. Are you continually seeking new skills, tools, and techniques to eliminate the stress of misunderstandings, miscommunications, missed opportunities?

Step 3. Action

The *Action* step to change is often the most difficult. There's a little saying, "If you always do what you've always done, you'll always get what you've always got." Continuing to do the same thing the same way will consistently take you nowhere. If you are going to give stress a rest, move it away from you, or manage it better, then you have to take action. Here is a simple technique to help move us in the direction of taking action. Complete these two phrases.

I want to . . .

so that . . .

You need to define what is causing you stress and then give yourself a benefit that will result from taking action. This technique is so simple, and works, because you are taking control of the "want to" by showing yourself the benefits and results of your own actions. Here are some real-life examples from clients I have worked with.

I want to speak with more confidence, clarity and professionalism...

so that I will feel more comfortable with customers.

I want to learn how to be more effective in handling internal issues of management . . .

so that I can let go of this job when I leave at the end of the day.

I want to learn how to stay calm in intense professional circumstances . . .

so that I can build better relationships with my clients.

I want to learn how to further my career without sacrificing family time . . .

so that I will have balance in both areas of my life.

I want to be able to respond and communicate effectively in situations that take me by surprise . . .

so that I don't feel and present myself as flustered, defeated, and guilty.

Realizing your own, "*I want to . . . so that*" will help move yourself into taking action. I love this quote from the Reverend Robert Schuller, "Today's decisions are tomorrow's realities." What we decide to put into action today, through words, deeds, attitudes, communication, and emotions, will determine our tomorrows.

Here is my personal "*I want to . . . so that*":

I want to build better relationships with people in my personal life, value their uniqueness, respect their points of view, and communicate more clearly to understand and to be understood . . .

so that I can have peace of mind, long-lasting relationships, good health, and less stress.

Take a moment to fill in your *I want to . . . so that.*

Professional area of my life
I want to:

_____

_____

_____

so that:

_____

_____

_____

Personal area of my life
I want to:

_____

_____

_____

so that:

_____

_____

_____

It is important to understand that not one of the three steps to moving stress away from you can stand alone. If you have a heartfelt need to reduce stress in your life, you will have the motivation to gain new skills and knowledge. Putting those skills into action requires making necessary changes.

As you make these changes, you will begin a new course of learning. Here are some prime examples of real life lessons learned.

The Q-Tip Lesson:
Quit
Taking
It
Personally

Our stress level goes up when we start doubting and thinking negatively. These preconceived thoughts or fears may not be true. When words are spoken or actions taken based on assumptions, miscommunication and conflict will elevate the stress level. Look at the following examples, and reflect on the times you need to pick up the Q-Tip!

"I must have said or done something wrong to not be included in the design phase of the Owens Project. I thought they were counting on my advice."

Pick up the Q-Tip.

"Why am I always the last one to be informed of the changes around here? It just isn't fair."

Pick up the Q-Tip.

"They said they were going to be here. I wonder if I offended them in some way."

Pick up the Q-Tip.

"The grandkids always find time for their friends and all their sports. Obviously we don't count."

Pick up the Q-Tip.

"I would love to have the Joneses over for a backyard barbecue, but they would probably rather be with the Snyders."

Pick up the Q-Tip.

"They purposely planned the thirty-fifth anniversary celebration on that weekend, knowing I was going to be out of town."

Pick up the Q-Tip.

"My co-workers never ask me to join them for lunch."

Pick up the Q-Tip.

Real Life Lesson Learned: Pick up the Q-Tip. Quit Taking It Personally.

The Tree Frog Lesson:

The air was fresh and the mountain stream cool and rushing. We were having the time of our lives, surfing in a river just outside of Gatlinburg, Tennessee. Our friends, George and MaryAnn, were making sure that we experienced every molecule of Gatlinburg and the majestic Smokey Mountains — in three days! We hiked winding paths that led to the most awesome waterfalls. We rode ski lifts to the top of the mountain and experienced the breathtaking beauty. We found a historic settlement where we hauled out the coolers, spread the blankets in the grass, and had a mountainside picnic under the shade trees.

Are you getting the picture? Great friends, fun, and adventure; and we were going to do it all — in three days. This goal would require late nights and early mornings, and would be accomplished by four people in one car on winding roads and steep climbs.

Driving back from an adventurous day, tired and hungry, we heard a loud chirping noise from outside the car windows.

Someone suggested it was crickets.

"No, it's not crickets. It's frogs croaking."

"It's crickets; frogs don't sound like that."

"It's tree frogs. That's what it is."

"Tree frogs? No way!"

There we were; four adults in one car, getting stressed about this chirping noise.

From the front seat, George made a wise and profound statement:

"If you want to think they are frogs, then they are frogs.

If you want to think they are crickets, then they are crickets.

If you want to think they are tree frogs, then they are tree frogs."

My husband and I have used George's tree frog philosophy many times when stress seems to mount up because of different points of view.

Real Life Lesson Learned: Let others be right. Is it really going to matter in ten years, ten minutes?

The Desk to Desk Lesson:

For six months Bill and Mary have accomplished the assigned responsibility of merging information from each of their departments into a master report, a major, high-stress-level project because of the detailed facts and accuracy required.

The deadlines have been met, the reports correct and approved each month. However, the past two months have been exceedingly frustrating for Bill. Mary has waited until the latest deadline to get her portion of the report completed, which adds mounting tension and last minute pressure for any corrections, additions or re-writes. Delays like this could jeopardize the quality and accuracy required and put their jobs at risk.

If Bill says nothing, Mary may continue to deliver her portion of the report later and later each month. Bill's stress and frustration will heighten.

Bill chooses to take the professional, assertive approach. He realizes that saying nothing could lead to his becoming aggressive in his communication and behavior.

"As you know Mary, we've been able to meet our target deadlines for the Wilmington Report every month since it has been assigned to us. I think we can give ourselves a pat on the back for our competency. It seems we have run into some unexpected updates the last two months, putting us under added pressure. What are your thoughts about moving our deadline up three days from the cutoff, giving us some cushion time, or getting together on the 25th of each month for a five-minute overview of our individual reports before we merge the information?"

Bill has professionally and assertively approached a stressful, touchy situation and has maintained the working relationship needed to meet the expectations placed on them. By using this approach, Bill has maintained respect for himself and Mary, reduced the level of Mary's defensiveness, and prevented conflict from escalating.

Real Life Lesson Learned: Use assertive communication skills to address difficult situations rather than avoiding them or allowing them to become stressful.

The Brick Wall Lesson:

Have you ever felt as if you were running into a brick wall? Not a ten-foot-high brick wall, but a wall that appears to be a dead end that you keep slamming into. It is stressful and it hurts.

Brick Walls can happen in every area of life. Some Brick Walls are sudden and unexpected, while others are built brick by brick, year after year.

Actor Christopher Reeves' life was instantly changed in May of 1995. At an equestrian event in Culpeper, Virginia, he was thrown from his horse and instantly paralyzed from the neck down. In a flash of a second, his personal dreams, his acting career, and his physical abilities were slammed into a Brick Wall.

For twenty-four years I had a career, working with 250 sales associates, a management team, and an office staff. I thought I would have that job for as long as I wanted it. Slowly, major corporate bricks began to pile up. I continued to run into that growing Brick Wall for three years, until the physical and mental stress took its toll on me.

My friend Sharon was holding onto her dream of moving back to California. She loved everything about living near the ocean: palm trees, warm sunshine, beaches. She had wonderful memories of the West Coast. So wonderful were her West Coast memories, they were keeping her enjoyment of her current locale to a minimum.

Brick Walls all look different. Some will place themselves suddenly and without warning in front of us. Others will be built up before us while we struggle against them. Still others will be erected by us, stifling our own progress. They may be made of people, places, money, habits, events, or just about anything that can hold us back. But all Brick Walls give us opportunities to make important decisions. We can continue to keep hanging on and beating ourselves up with misery or pain, or we can use the Brick Wall Strategy:

If you don't like something, work to
  Change it.
  If you can't change it, work to
  Accept It.
  If you can't accept it, work to
  Leave or let go.

There are people, situations, and things that we cannot control. We have to analyze what we can change and what we cannot. Sometimes we just have to let go. If we let go, the accepting of our Brick Wall is much easier.

Christopher Reeves has been an inspiring example of using the Brick Wall Strategy when adversity comes quickly and unexpectedly. He has put incredible energy and time into supporting the research efforts of doctors and scientists. It is a personal mission of his to help establish what can and cannot be changed for individuals with severe spinal cord injuries. He has accepted his current condition and works within those parameters, but is confident that a cure is on the horizon. In his book, *Still Me*, Reeves calls it "realistic optimism."

After twenty-four years, I took a good look at the bricks being laid in front of me. I stacked the things I could change next to the things I was unable to change. Then I asked myself if I could accept what I could not control or would it continue to be stressful. I came to the conclusion that I needed to make some changes, to let go and move in a different direction. That was a very scary decision. The first step I took was to make an appointment with a resume writer. She helped me realize my professional strengths and to see new opportunities. That was five years ago and I am so glad I'm not still running into that Brick Wall.

My friend Sharon decided to exert a purposeful effort toward discovering all the great aspects of where she is living now. She added them up and realized she is in the best location for her and her family at this point in her life. Sharon has found new interests and has built wonderful friendships and is now fully able to enjoy making memories in this new place she calls home. She still plans to vacation in sunny

California; but going back will no longer mean facing her Brick Wall.

Real Life Lesson Learned: Change. Accept. Leave or Let Go.

Conclusion:

"Would you like to move stress away from you?" I'll bet that your answer is the same as it was when you began reading this chapter . . . "Yes!" We do stress ourselves and each other, but there are specific steps that you can take today to start making significant changes in your personal and professional life to move stress away from you. Commit yourself to these three steps:

Step 1. A Heartfelt Need

Step 2. New Skills and Knowledge

Step 3. Action

In picking up the book and focusing on this chapter, you have already exhibited a heartfelt need to reduce the stress in your life. You are now armed with four valuable life lessons that I have outlined. You have gained new skills and knowledge. I urge you to follow your personal or professional, *"I want to . . . so that"* and take action today. You can, and will, move stress away from you and begin on a more fulfilling life journey. God speed!

ABOUT
GERRY GRINOLD

*G*erry *Grinold, founder of Next Step Solutions, Inc., is an internationally recognized personal development trainer. Her popular seminars
are known for giving you what you need to get you where you want to go.
Gerry's dynamic presentation style grabs your attention, gives you direction and equips you with the necessary tools for sustained success. Her 24
year career working with 250 sales associates and a diverse management
team in a fast-paced office has given her a unique perspective. She shares
insights and secrets for building relationships, communicating effectively,
managing stress and providing exceptional customer service.*

*Gerry has a strong sense of what it takes to produce winning
outcomes. Her messages are personal, professional and powerful! To stay
current with new trends and ideas, Gerry is an active participant in the
National Speakers Association, Michigan Business & Professional
Association, and Mothers March of Dimes.*

Contact Information:
Gerry Grinold
Next Step Solutions, Inc.
1423 W. Kinsel Highway
Charlotte MI 48813
Phone: (517) 543-7004
Fax: (517) 543-2099
E-mail: grinold@voyager.net

TAKING CARE OF YOURSELF SO YOU HAVE WHAT IT TAKES TO TAKE CARE OF OTHERS

by Holly Stiel

When I was eighteen years old my father said to me, "You know, Holly, I never worry about you because I don't think anyone will ever take better care of you than you!" How prophetic that statement was as I have spent the past 27 years becoming an expert in the art of self-care!

I was just twenty-four years young when a series of emotional traumas in quick succession left me feeling lost, alone, and frightened. A friend took me to hear a very powerful speaker named Raymond Charles Barker. I remember his asking, "Do any of you think your life is a movie?" I could relate, although my life was more like a soap opera than a movie. I sat up attentively.

The next thing I heard changed my life. "When are you going to get it — you're the projector, not the screen!" he declared. Wow! Before that moment I hadn't realized I had choices. Life was what happened to you. That was the beginning of my journey. Although willing, there's been a fair share of kicking and screaming down the path of transformation.

My natural appetite for self-care was nourished by my need to preserve my health and sanity in a very stressful job that I loved despite the pressure. I spent 17 years as a hotel concierge helping 300 people a day. That meant sometimes being on two phones, with more people standing in front of me (not always patiently) waiting for answers. I knew if I didn't take some time to re-energize, I would burn out before my fortieth birthday.

How are you replenishing yourself? What are you doing to take care of you? It's a scientific law that if you continually draw water from a well without replenishing it, eventually it will run dry. The airlines have it right when they say, "Secure your own oxygen mask before attempting to help others." It is difficult, perhaps impossible, to separate self-care from self-love. No technique of self-care works unless the underlying tenet is self-love and nurturing.

It is important to understand what self-care is and is not. It seems like a paradox, but self-care is not about being a narcissist. Taking care of oneself is how we can contribute more love to others. Self-care happens in relationships as well as in solitude. It is about being kind and tender with ourselves. It is a lifelong commitment and it is always in process. It is not about being selfish, feeling guilty, or extreme discipline. It is not about money or expensive treatments (while those are nice, they are optional).

Your own personal degree of self-love will have a direct effect on your ability to self-nurture. The odd thing is self-love doesn't come all that naturally. It is in a constant battle with your inner voice, wanting to sabotage you. The human mind is amazing! Over the years I have learned to love myself — flaws, cellulite, the entire package. I'm much happier now.

I began the process by noticing the ways I sabotaged myself. Some classics included critical self-talk designed to make me doubt myself by negating compliments, comparing myself to others, saying yes when I really wanted to say no, not following through on the promises I made to myself, and staying in toxic relationships. It takes a conscious effort to shift your own inner conversation to one of kindness and to set the kind of boundaries needed to allow only the people and thoughts that serve you to be in your life.

One of the typical ways to sabotage your self-care is by not allowing yourself to play. In some cultures, people who don't rest are considered odd. In our culture, we seem to be in the midst of a time famine and everyone is in a permanent state of frenzy. A terrific way to break this cycle is to remember what you did as a child to play. Ask yourself that very question, "What did I do as a child to play?" When I answered that question, something was rekindled that changed my life and was highly nurturing. My answers including ice skating, riding a bike, and swimming. As I lived in San Francisco, riding a bike up and down hills didn't seem much fun. There were no skating rinks nearby so I tried swimming. I remembered how much I had enjoyed it as a child, and it turned out I enjoyed it very much as an adult.

Is there something in your life that you did as child that you could do as an adult? If there is, make an appointment with yourself to do it, and, no matter what, don't break the appointment. It is important to schedule your self-care.

I have found a self-care technique that is a great way to give stress a rest. You can even look at it as a daily vacation, a journey to a quiet and peaceful place.

Take a Daily Vacation —
A journey to a quiet and peaceful place

Meditation can be a daunting concept. Does the thought fill you with visions of yogis leading a life of solitude in a mountain retreat? It did me. I'm so glad I didn't let my preconceptions prevent me from exploring this powerful, simple, and enormously effective practice. Regular meditation time is actually a blessing and the best thing busy people can do to create sanity and peace in a frantic world. Interestingly, the root word for mediation is the same as the root word for medicine.

I would never say that meditation is an easy thing to do. Simple, yes. Easy, no. As a matter of fact, clearing the mind is one of the most difficult practices to master in life. Don't worry, however, there is good news. You don't have to master it. That is why it is called a practice. One day I hope to write an article about the wonders of having a clear mind (the ultimate goal of meditation). That day has not yet arrived.

Today, I can share with you the wonders of engaging in a daily practice of mindful meditation. My mind is still full, but highly focused. The benefits have been enormous, as I continue to develop my inner life

— a calm and friendly relationship with myself that I never had before I began this practice. It is the way I begin my day, and the benefits manifest throughout the day, especially if I close my eyes, take a deep breath (the access point is through the breath) and go back to those quiet and precious moments just after rising.

I had heard about the benefits of meditation for years, read books, and tried it several times, always failing miserably, fidgeting, thinking of everything under the sun — my busy mind was on full throttle. I tried meditation retreats, classes, and audiotapes and I just didn't "get it." I was thrilled when I learned about walking meditation. At least I could do something, and occasionally I would be mindful and pay complete attention to my breath, my steps, and my surroundings. I was not, however, consistent.

I think one of the most interesting things about learning, especially where personal growth is concerned, is that even though we know the information and want to act on it, our behavior doesn't reflect the changes we say we want. Then one day we hear the information again, maybe in a new way, perhaps from a new person. Maybe we are finally ready to hear it. Maybe it's the theory at work, that when the student is ready the teacher appears.

Whatever the reason, a yoga teacher at the Spa at Lake Austin not only gave me some tools, but the context that turned the knowledge into action. Thank you, Tanya; I am forever grateful to you for helping to guide me on this path of self-love, relaxation, and serenity. I am delighted to share what I learned and what I now practice daily in the hopes that I may be a teacher for you, the readers. Please know that you can use all of these ideas, or take just one or two and create your own morning mindfulness. I do not claim to be all-knowing. Quite the contrary . . . I only claim to know enough that I am compelled to share it. As a matter of fact, the more I learn, the less I know, and this inspires me to keep learning.

The Context

Why did Tanya's meditation class "click" when all others had failed? I believe it was the context she put it in, giving me a reason to meditate beyond the promise of feeling better. I felt fine without it or so

I thought. Tanya used a metaphor of the painting, "The Three Graces," to explain the context of meditation. The painting is of three women, one with her back to the viewer, one in a half turn, and one facing fully front. The first woman represented youth, moving forward with abandon. The second represented mid-life, having felt life's turning points and being sidelined by its sorrows. The third represented the fullness of life, moving forward into old age and finally crossing over. It was in this fullness of life that she explained the yearning to know oneself fully, and to shed the trappings of the material world as the markers of success. If joy and self-esteem has been based on job status, good looks, and accomplishments, this third phase of life presented a pretty bleak picture. The antidote was to develop a deep and secure inner life, so the reactions and responses of the outside world matter less and less.

No more cat calls from construction workers? Who cares? I am at peace and have a great relationship with myself. This is especially important for women who, "at a certain age," begin to feel invisible in our culture. Hearing this information at 51, with the reality of "the change" ever present, hot flash to hot flash, I was inspired to spring into action. I no longer thought I *should* meditate. I *chose* to meditate, I *wanted* to. I couldn't wait to begin this personal romance. I kept thinking of Oscar Wilde saying "Love yourself and you'll have a relationship that will last forever."

The Practice
The timing — first thing in the morning

All my other attempts had failed because I didn't meditate as my very first activity. Once I started my day, I simply couldn't stop. Now I sit first thing and start my day with peace and not a hustle-bustle. There is no shortage of hustle-bustle in daily life. However, there is a shortage of peace, groundedness, and calm. I would be experiencing busyness soon enough. Now was my time for bliss. Once I learned how to relax, it was amazing to be able to access that same peace and calm within myself any time during the day that I chose.

Develop the circuitry through daily practice and it's yours anytime.

The other obvious benefit to meditating first thing in the morning is that you are already in a relaxed state. Make sure you are sitting comfortably in a chair or on meditation pillows on the floor. Don't lie down or the possibility exists that you will fall back to sleep. You need to be awake to meditate.

Light a candle

This simple act is symbolic of being in the light. It signals the beginning of your special time with yourself. I like to use aromatherapy candles or an infuser which has a place for a candle underneath and water infused with aroma oils on top. The aroma oils will help you to focus, as breathing in the scent of lavender or other scents that have calming properties add to the enjoyment of your personal retreat from the busyness of life on earth.

Begin morning mindfulness

An easy way to begin is to hold both hands in the air in front of you, elbows bent, palms facing out. Recite the following mantra ten times. Each time you recite it, put your thought into a different finger. This will keep you focused. Start with the pinkie finger and say, "I am open to you, God, come sit in my heart." Next, put your attention on the ring finger and say, "I am open to you, God, come sit in my heart." Continue until you have repeated it ten times, once for each finger. At this point, you will feel relaxed and ready to drop your hands in your lap and spend a few minutes or moments just listening to your breath.

Listen to your breath; be aware of your breath. Try to breathe fully. Stomach extended as you inhale, contracted on the exhale. You can say a mantra or concentrate on a word. I use the word "*love*," for that is what I wish to give and to receive.

Begin a mindful prayer. It is a Buddhist practice and a beautiful way to fuel yourself for being in the world. It is done six times, six rounds of the same prayer said for different people and for different reasons. The first round is for yourself, the second for your significant other or close loved one, the third for a friend, the fourth for an acquaintance, the fifth for an enemy, and the sixth for the universe.

Imagine yourself in your mind's eye and silently say, "May I be filled with peace and calm. May I bloom and may I blossom. May I move forward without fear. May I heal in loving."

Imagine your loved one or significant other in your mind's eye and repeat the four verses of the prayer. This time, substitute their name for yours.

Imagine a friend in your mind's eye, and repeat the prayer using that person's name. Try to think of different friends every day. I am so happy to send friends a prayer it makes me smile.

Imagine an acquaintance in your mind's eye (bank teller, grocery clerk, waiter, etc.). This is my favorite part as it makes me feel the oneness of all of us instead of the separateness that our culture breeds. I actually look forward to finding the person I'll send a prayer to the next morning. I look for them as I run errands or travel.

Imagine an enemy in your mind's eye (sometimes I imagine anyone I have ever hurt or who wishes to hurt me). This is the most difficult part of the prayer as I sometimes don't want to wish that my enemies will bloom and blossom. I do it anyway. It helps me to add the thought, "May they bloom and blossom so that they no longer have the need to hurt others."

Say the prayer for the universe. At this point, you may choose to stop, do a few grounding breaths and begin your day.

If you find your mind wandering, imagine you are sitting in the middle of a river. Let the thought flow down the river past you and let it float away from you down the river (back to your mindful time). Once you accept that you cannot meditate (clear your mind), it can begin to work because the quiet time is a place that you don't have to be success-oriented.

If you choose to continue, you can take the opportunity of this quiet and reflective time to send a healing prayer to the people you know who are ill and wish them love. I then start the process of opening my seven major energy centers or chakras, taken from ancient Indian wisdom. I take deep grounding breaths, in through the nose and out through the mouth. Remember it is through the breath that we access the light. With every inhale, I visualize a spark of color at the energy center I am focusing on, and with the exhale I begin to spin that spark of color clockwise, placing the thought or "energy" I wish to hold for that center. Imagine, each one as a lotus flower; the first chakra has the least amount of petals, the seventh has the most.

First chakra is the base of the spine. The color is red and the thought is, "I am safe."

Second chakra is just below the navel — the color is orange and the thought is, "I am joyous and experience pleasure."

The third chakra is the solar plexus, the color is yellow, and the thought is, "I embrace my power."

The fourth chakra is the heart, the color is green, and the thought is, "My heart is open to the fullness of life."

The fifth chakra is the throat, the color is light blue, and the thought is, "I speak my word; I express myself fully."

The sixth chakra is the third eye, the color is deep indigo, and the thought is, "I am present to this moment. I stay present to each moment knowing the universe wants only the best for me."

The seventh chakra is at the crown of the head. The color is lavender, and the thought is "I am grateful and open to the assistance of the higher worlds." At this time I welcome my angels, spirit guides, and friends and have been known to dialogue with them, thanking them for their guidance, friendship, and support.

I take two deep breaths, imagining my rainbow of energy from the top of my head down to my first chakra, then from my first up to my seventh. I visualize for a moment my hopes and dreams for that day and my bigger-picture dreams of the future. I am then ready to do some grounding breaths. Feeling fully grounded, blessed and protected, I am tempted to stay in this state, but I know I must come out so I slowly open my eyes, blow out the candle and go about my daily activities. I am happy to wake up 30 minutes earlier to partake in this beautiful inner journey that honors the blessings in my life, including myself.

Ideas that Take Less than 20 Minutes
to Expand Our Definition of Wealth and Create Balance

If you are so pressed for time that you couldn't possibly take 20 minutes for yourself, here are ideas that take less than 20 minutes, and ideas that take no more than two minutes.

- Be in nature. Walk without purpose, noticing how everything is connected.
- Stop in awe and admire the natural beauty that surrounds us. Say thank you.
- Read something inspiring daily.
- Pick one word to contemplate each week. Whenever you feel rushed or stressed, bring yourself back to that word, i.e. grace, light, harmony, calm.
- Go to a park and just sit.
- Try a walking meditation for 10-20 minutes. Do not speak; just notice the air, your breath, the feel of the ground beneath your feet. Notice your pace, posture, surroundings. Walk with consciousness and quiet the mind.
- Arrange flowers in a vase. Make fresh flowers a priority in your life. Buy them for yourself every week.
- Create a sacred space on a mantle or dresser, and place things there that remind you to honor what is truly important.
- Go to a farmers' market and stroll down the aisles. Slow your pace.
- Take a luxurious bath in aroma oils. Nothing soothes like hot water.
- One day a week start the morning with journaling, just free writing about whatever comes to your mind.
- Eat a meal in silence.

Ideas that Take Two Minutes or Less
Finding the Sacred in the Midst of the Insane

- Make a memory.
- Light a candle.

- Say a blessing before a meal.
- Say a blessing for a friend, family member, or loved one.
  May you be wise.
  May you feel love.
  May you be happy.
- Spread joy and make a conscious effort to say something kind. Ask yourself, "Does my behavior merit another day?"
- When you chop, chop. Bring your awareness to the task at hand.
- Start the day with the words, "I love you."
- Take three joy breaths.
- Release something you have when you purchase something new. Too much clutter and too many possessions are stressful and possess you.
- Choose one spot that reminds you of these ideas, like a door handle. Every time you touch it, you remember.
- Take a deep breath.
- Stretch while waiting in line.
- Flick off negative energy.

What's Your Excuse?

There are always a million reasons to keep going and never enough reasons to stop and rest. Yet, it's no secret that some of the best ideas and greatest discoveries in human history have been incubated while the mind is on sabbatical.

Sir Isaac Newton discovered the law of gravity while sitting under a tree. Benjamin Franklin invented the lightning rod while flying a kite. Albert Einstein pondered the riddle of the universe while a cat purred contentedly in his lap.

When we take time to rejuvenate, we are more creative and productive. So, don't do something . . . sit there.

ABOUT
HOLLY STIEL

*H*olly Stiel is an internationally recognized expert on service. She is an author, professional speaker and seminar leader who teaches "the art of customer service from the inside out." Holly is a world-renowned leader in concierge service training. For sixteen years she served as a hotel concierge, providing for as many as 300 customers a day. She single-handedly started the concierge department at San Francisco's Grand Hyatt. Holly was the first American woman admitted to the exclusive international concierges' association, Les Clefs d'Or, and was a founding member of the association in the U.S.

Holly knows the agony and the ecstasy of customer service first hand and believes that good service is an art. She has written three books: Ultimate Service *(the definitive textbook for the concierge profession);* Thank You Very Much *(a book for anyone who has ever asked, "May I help you?");* The Neon Signs of Service *(getting to the heart of the matter in customer service). As a professional speaker, Holly has fascinated audiences of 3 to 3,000 in the U.S., Canada, Asia, Mexico and South Africa. She was the first woman and non-corporate executive to receive the Distinguished Visiting Professor award from Johnson & Wales University. Her clients include Nordstrom, Bellagio Hotel & Resort, Motorola, Bank of America, Compaq, Bail Associates and Pebble Beach Corporation.*

Contact Information:
Holly Stiel
Holly Speaks
728 Bay Road
Mill Valley, CA 94941
Phone: (415) 383-4220
Fax: (415) 383-1503
E-mail: HollySpeaks@aol.com
Website: www.ThankYouVeryMuchInc.com

BALANCE OR BURNOUT?
40 Quick and Easy Tools and Tips for Life Balance

by Celeste Jonson

B alance or burnout? That really is an important question we must ask ourselves as we live and work in this era when the pace is fast, the demands are high, and change is the only constant denominator.

Life Balance

We hear a lot about life balance these days but what exactly is it? One definition might be "Successfully fulfilling the expectations and responsibilities in the workplace while simultaneously and effectively meeting your personal and family needs, handling unexpected crises, and coping with the perpetual changes of life." At times it may feel out of reach or completely impossible, and indeed it may be, but certainly it is possible to have more balance and less burnout if we proactively make the efforts to do so. So many of us simply continue doing what we've always done and react to what comes our way. Our lives are often like running on the proverbial treadmill — running steadily faster and up and down hills yet going nowhere, seeing nothing different, learning nothing new, and enjoying the life experience less and less. Does this sound familiar?

Signs of Burnout

Carol, a successful account representative, is a single mother who wakes up at 7 a.m. — too late to exercise as she had planned. She starts the coffee and grabs a donut. She goes to wake up two reluctant kids, begins to get dressed, and helps her unorganized and groggy kids to do likewise. Back in the kitchen it's Pop Tarts and milk for the kids and the making of school lunches. Then it's off to drop the kids at school and day care, drop the car at the dealership for service, get a rental car, and join the rush hour traffic as she heads to her office.

Carol's manager just called an emergency meeting about the impending merger that is rumored to mean a layoff of 15 percent of the staff and a restructuring of territories. Will she be one of the victims or survivors? Either way, she wonders how she will make ends meet.

The rest of her day consists of loads of telephone calls, a couple of scheduled and several unscheduled internal meetings, and outside appointments with clients. The unexpected morning meeting has pushed everything back and she's now running behind.

Oh no, it's already 5:30 p.m., traffic is heavy and she needs to pick the kids up across town before 6:30 p.m. or else she is charged $10 for every five minutes she's late. However, she has yet to pick up her car from the shop. At least 80 percent of the things she wanted to complete today still need to be done, even though she worked straight through lunch. Carol is also painfully aware that, once she arrives home, she has another whole shift to work including dinner, clean up, homework to monitor, and additional paperwork to complete before an important meeting tomorrow.

Overloaded, overextended, and stressed — all the makings of potential burnout. Do you know anyone like this? Do you ever look in the mirror at someone like this?

Burnout. Are you a candidate?

Burnout can be viewed as a state of mental, physical, and spiritual exhaustion caused by unrelenting, unmanaged, or mismanaged stress. It is often recognized as a loss of energy and enthusiasm for life, overwhelming pessimism with tendencies for depression, and no clear focus or sense of purpose and direction.

Those affected, often high achievers, are having heart attacks and ulcers at alarming rates. There are over 12 million alcoholics in the United States and over 13 billion doses of tranquilizers, amphetamines, and barbiturates prescribed annually. So many illnesses are directly affected by excessive stress. The prime candidates often overextend themselves, won't or don't know how to ask for help, are not clear of what's most important, are indecisive, and are in less-than-optimal health.

Have we given up too much to have it all?

We also buy into the hype of "having it all," especially from a financial and economic standpoint. Without much thought, resulting in no strategy, we operate from a crisis management standpoint, focusing on the current demanding aspect of our lives (usually work and finances) at the expense of other, perhaps even more important ones. The intent is to improve the quality of life for our family and ourselves; only we discover that in that quest we have sacrificed the very thing we say we are working for.

We think, "If we can only obtain that ultimate degree of success meriting prestige and financial rewards, we can have that house, that car, afford that vacation, wear those clothes, give more to our children and loved ones, etc." So we give it all we've got and we often end up so busy and stressed, we don't have time to truly enjoy that improved "quality" of life, i.e., time spent with our children while they are children to watch them play in the expensive gym shoes we bought them, or quality time spent on building that fulfilling relationship with our significant other, or that irreplaceable time to spend with our aging parents — or simply time to rest and rejuvenate.

Yes, when we choose to have it all, especially financially, we've often chosen to give up some important things that money can't buy. Life is about choices and even sacrifices and some of them are very difficult — even seemingly impossible — but as we face these difficult decisions and try to indeed do and have it all, I must pose the question, "Have we given up too much to have it all"?

I have a passion for this topic because for a long time I was the poster girl for imbalance. That "make it happen — can do" attitude, which is a great characteristic for success, can get you in trouble if you don't know how to effectively balance it with knowing how and when to say no. It became so bad that the last time they were updating Webster's dictionary I was asked for a photo to be included next to the word "imbalance." Well, not really, but I felt like it would have been very appropriate. Yes, I was the poster girl, and it seems that some of you are vying for that position.

Using burnout as an acronym, I define burnout as being:

B — Bombarded with babies, bosses and/or boyfriends combined with . . .

U — Unrealistic expectations (often self-imposed).

R — Running on the proverbial treadmill of life, going nowhere fast with . . .

N — No clarity of what's really most important, no focus, no joy, and no rest.

O — Overextended, out of control, and out of shape.

U — Unhappy, unfulfilled, with a tendency for ulcers and . . .

T — Tears . . . just flat out tired!

Where do you stand? Are you a candidate for burnout? If any of this sounds like someone you know, intimately perhaps, don't fret. Instead, read on. Help is on the way.

We are much too blessed to be stressed.

We have the power and even the obligation to live our lives with some semblance of order and direction vs. being chaotic and scattered. Yes, we have the power because we have the freedom of choice. We can choose to do different things or, better yet, choose not to do things that cause undue stress. We can choose to optimize our health — to take care of this incredible gift we've been given that houses our spirit and soul. We know we function better under any circumstances when we feel good, when we've had a good night's sleep, when our system is flushed of high fat and toxic foods. Those days when we're feeling our best, nothing seems to bother us. We have a choice to have more of those days than any other.

We have a choice to look to God, our creator, to give us some directions and instructions as it relates to what we were created for. I am convinced that if more of us made decisions in our lives and operated from our strength — from what it is that is in our hearts and perhaps even our DNA, there would be a lot less stress and a lot more happy and successful people. Think about it. If we were doing what we love to do — what we are naturally talented and inclined to do, we could minimize, if not get rid of, the mindset of "hump day" or "living for the weekend" or the fact that there are more heart attacks on Monday mornings between 9 a.m. and 10 a.m. than any other time of the week — the beginning of the work week for most. There certainly would be a greater collective sense of balance and order in the world and a lot less stress.

As for obligation, we must consider the fact that our behavior affects those around us whether we're at home, at work, while driving, or other places. Isn't it true that if our spouse or other family member comes home agitated and stressed from the day that we feel it and are often affected by it? Likewise, if a client, customer or co-worker is in a frenzy, that can and often affects us. We are certainly impacted by the people we are in close proximity with and they by us. Therefore we have an obligation, a responsibility, and, I dare say, an opportunity to literally affect the world — at the very least our immediate world by getting a handle on our own stress. We can and should let our balance be the pebble that begins the ripple effect in our environment and not the other way around. This reminds me of a quote that Martin Luther King often stated. He said, "We are in an inescapable network of mutuality — a single garment of destiny. And what affects one directly, affects all indirectly." Yes, we are much too blessed to be stressed.

Life Balance

Optimal life balance requires that we take care of ourselves — mind, body and spirit. At the same time, a balanced life means enjoying time with your family and friends, participating in meaningful work, enjoying financial solvency, and contributing to the health and welfare of our community. I call these areas *Fundamental Components of Life Management.*

Balance does not mean that each area has an equal allocation of our time, energy, and focus. That would be nearly impossible. As balance is not a static state, there are occasions when "temporary imbalance" is appropriate. The key to remember — it should only be "temporary," and we must have a plan to counterbalance it.

Some of us rush through life so fast that we not only forget where we've been, but we also forget where we're going. What's exciting about life, however, is that every morning offers a brand new day with unlimited possibilities. Yesterday's mistakes and regrets belong to yesterday. Today is a clean slate, a chance to start over, to do or become anything you want, a chance to go for it! Stop sprinting. Pace yourself. Slow down. Jump into life with both feet and enjoy it! Go forward, head held high, choosing balance and expecting the best . . . you may be surprised at how often that's exactly what you'll get.

With time being a premium, here are *40 Quick and Easy Tools and Tips for Life Balance*, excerpts from my book entitled *Life Balance: 150 Quick & Easy Tools & Tips*. I've broken them down into the various *Fundamental Components of Life Management* to provide more clarity and focus. You'll note that many of these tips are common knowledge; however, they are not always commonly practiced. You want more balance and less burnout? Try implementing one idea a day for a month or so and begin making balance a new success habit for life.

Balance Basics
(*Fundamental Principles of Balance*)

1. *Believe balance is possible.* If you believe it's only a "nice idea," you won't do what it takes to get more of it. And believe it to the point of expectation because then and only then will your behavior change. When you expect it to rain, you carry an umbrella. When you expect company to come, you clean up. When you expect more

balance in your life, you make different choices.

2. *Accept the fact that you cannot do everything that is available to you.*
   We have more options today in all aspects of our lives than ever
   before in history. That in itself is a wonderful fact; however, trying to
   act on and take advantage of them all can lead us straight to burnout.

3. *Ask yourself, "What's most important to me?" "What are my priorities in life?"* This is such a critical and essential component to
   gaining more balance in your life. If you're clear about what's most
   important and your priorities, it's easier to make decisions as to how
   you will spend your time.

4. *Care and have courage enough to change your choices.* It's not
   enough to want to have more balance; it requires taking some
   action, and often it will be actions others may not like. You've been
   there for them, and now you want to do something else with your
   time. This may not go over so big with everyone and will require
   courage on your part.

5. *Establish support systems both personally and professionally.* Use
   them! Internationally known motivational speaker and my friend,
   Les Brown, has often said "Ask for help. Not because you're weak,
   but because you want to remain strong!" There are many people
   willing to help you, and it is your job to find them and begin utilizing their services.

A Journey Within
(Spiritual Awareness, Growth and Direction)

6. *Get and keep things in perspective.* Take the time to look at what
   you already have vs. what you don't have. It's expressing what has
   been called "an attitude of gratitude." Sometimes we cannot see the
   lush forest in our lives for looking at the one challenging tree that's
   in our face. Step back from the tree and realize this immediate issue
   or matter that is stressing you may not be as significant as it appears
   when you consider the big picture.

7. *Recognize and tap into the creative and directing power of God.* Set

aside at least ten minutes of quiet time daily — preferably in the morning. The ideal place to do so is either outdoors or near a window looking outdoors where you are reminded of this power who created nature that is greater than you. Pray, meditate, ask for guidance, and listen. This is a really powerful source for countering stress and fostering balance. You see, how you start the day sets the tone for how the rest of the day will go.

8. *Capture your thoughts and feelings in a journal.* It's a great stress diffuser and helps you process your anxiety. The other great benefit is that it's less expensive than a therapist and rivals the effectiveness.

9. *Sing a song.* Sing lots of songs! Be sure the words are upbeat and encouraging and take advantage of the acoustics in the shower if you need them.

10. *Buy some fresh flowers for yourself — or someone else — or both.* It's amazing the power that flowers have on our spirit. Live plants can have the same effect.

Body Basics Plus
(Physical Health, Nutrition and Fitness)

11. *Do some form of exercise every day* even if it simply means walking an extra block or climbing an extra flight of stairs. Break a sweat. Be sure to alternate the exercise for variety and balance. You will enlist your team of endorphins to help you.

12. *Drink 8-10 glasses of water daily.* This helps flush out impurities from your body and reduces excess water in your system . . . one of the quickest ways to lose weight.

13. *Get your required amount of sleep at least three nights per week.* You'll handle everything better. There have been many reports lately about the importance of sleep as it relates to our overall health and the stress it puts on our system if we do not get an adequate amount.

14. *Get a massage!* I especially encourage men to do so because I've found most men have not even considered it. It is an awesome way to dissipate stress. Also, try an herbal wrap at least once — it helps

to detoxify your body.

15. *Practice deep breathing.* When you're under stress, your muscles tense, and your breathing becomes shallow and rapid. Deep and slow breathing is one of the simplest and best ways to stop this stress response. It really helps you relax. Standing, sitting or lying down, breathe in slowly through your nostrils, hold for a moment, and then exhale slowly through your mouth. Think of breathing in calm and breathing out stress.

16. *Take a hot bubble bath,* preferably with bath salts, which helps detoxify your body and relaxes your muscles. Epsom salt does the same thing. At the very least take a steaming hot shower. Use a loofah body scrubber. How refreshing!

Mind Over Matter
(Mental Alertness and Clarity)

17. *Watch your mental diet.* Remember you are what you eat — mentally too! Boycott negative news. Guard your mind at the gatepost of what you see and hear that may contribute unnecessarily to your stress. Digest information that will help you relax, create balance and do your job better verses things that will stress you more.

18. *Remember that your thinking determines your destiny.* Change your thinking, change your life. Think calm. Think control. Think positive. Think peace. What has been proven to help are visuals, i.e., pictures of your favorite place, a beach, mountains — whatever gives you a personal sense of peace or a mental picture of an optimistic outcome. Hold these visions as long and as frequently as possible.

19. *Help your overloaded mind by writing everything down in one location.* Trying to keep up with multiple calendars and date books only adds to confusion and your stress.

Cool, Calm, and Confident
(Emotional Wellness)

20. *Abandon the idea of perfection.* One challenge many people have with gaining and maintaining balance is trying to do everything —

all at once — and trying to do it all perfectly. Newsflash: Nothing and no one in the human race is perfect — get over it. Abandon the idea of perfection. Simply do your best and release the rest.

21. *Laugh often.* Find humor in situations. Buy a joke book or go to a comedy club. It will do wonders to help release the tension and heaviness of emotional "stuff."

22. *Have a release ceremony frequently.* Release negative thoughts and feelings about clients, colleagues, family, and friends. Dragging that baggage around requires too much energy and causes too much stress. Write down all the things getting on your last nerves — really think about them, decide to let them go, and then either tear that paper into small bits and burn it or flush it down the toilet. Release it. Let it go.

Creating Special Moments
(Relationships with Self, Family and Friends)

23. *Send a card to someone you know.* Isn't it a wonderful feeling when you receive a card in the mail instead of bills or marketing letters? When you make the effort to initiate this feeling for others, you can't help but feel good yourself. It's been said that you can't sprinkle perfume on someone else without getting some on yourself. The feeling is priceless.

24. *Call an old friend.* Catch up on old times. There is never enough time in the day to do everything that is available, and relationships that we say are important to us often get pushed to the back burner. Perhaps you can't do it every day but taking the time and making the effort to reconnect with special people adds a whole new dimension to the day-to-day stressors.

25. *Address, stamp, and file greeting cards in your tickler file* for mailing at the appropriate time. This is just a smart and efficient way to stay on top of things and spread joy systematically. It works!

26. *Do not take for granted the things and people closest to your heart.* Cling to them as you would your life, for without them, life is

meaningless. Show you care by what you say and do.

Satisfied and Solvent
(Meaningful Work and Financial Vitality)

27. *Be clear where you want to go but flexible on how you get there.*
Brian Tracy, a well-known speaker and author, has often said these
words. Being clear where we want to go is so fundamental to being
able to make optimal decisions as to how we spend our time.
However, it is also very important that we maintain some flexibility in our approach — being open to new and perhaps better ways of
doing things. We must be willing to change if we want to get better.

28. *Become debt free.* Live below your means. Money has always been a
source of stress for many. And generally it's the feeling of not having
enough that is at the root of most of it. It is said to be one of the leading
causes of problems in relationships. Being debt free is truly a wonderful feeling yet one that the average American never experiences. Our
culture encourages us to "charge it" and "buy now and pay later," and
we do. When you owe no one, your stress levels are greatly reduced and
it allows you so many more options. And one of the fundamental ways
to live without debt is to live below your means. Most of us live beyond
our means and are just a paycheck away from being on the street. If you
want to drastically reduce your stress, strive to be debt free.

29. *Consistently save.* This will make a significant difference in how you
view your circumstances. Having money in the bank, no matter how
small, makes a big difference in your sense of security. Even if you
earn a large sum of money, there is a big difference in your stress
level if you know you have something to fall back on if needed.

30. *Be a good steward of what you've been blessed with.* Use what you
have wisely. This is a lesson I've had to learn the hard way and continue
to be challenged with. It is especially tough when you work hard and
feel like you ought to be able to play hard. To some degree you should,
but it needs to be tempered if you again want to provide yourself with
a wonderful sense of preparedness, astuteness, and security.

The Joy of Giving
(Community Contribution & Service)

31. *Visit someone in the hospital or nursing home.* That will quickly put your challenges in perspective and will be a pick-me-up for them. Often we take for granted the simple ability to be in relatively good health and the ability to get around fairly easily. And we won't really know how valuable and joyous a visit can be until we are the ones being visited. Visit while you have the option.

32. *Give others a sense of contribution by letting them help you.* Sometimes we think we are being considerate and strong by not asking for or letting others help. We're so independent. Of course, there is something to be said about being able to stand on your own; however, there is also something to be said about allowing others the opportunity to have the joy that comes from giving. When we never let others help, we are prohibiting them from the satisfaction that is so rewarding. Let others help you.

33. *Help somebody and help yourself.* Do something for someone with no expectation of anything in return. Offer your professional skills, service and personal expertise to a local group who can't afford to pay you.

34. *Always under promise and over deliver.* It is less stressful and more rewarding when you deliver more than you promised. Keep this as your motto.

How to Rescue Yourself from Time Bandits
(Time/Event Management)

35. *Eliminate and delegate.* More times than not, all the things we say we need to do, we don't. Frequently re-evaluate your to-do list. Ask yourself, "Do I really need to do this? What will happen if I don't do this?" Eliminate all unnecessary items. Then go back through that list and identify items that you can delegate to others. Which items must you do and which items can you delegate?

36. *Learn to say no.* Re-evaluate your schedule and ask yourself, "Does this help me achieve my goals? Is this consistent with my priorities?

Must I say yes to everything asked of me?" The answer is often "*No!*" If it's inconsistent with your objective, say no — practice it! You may choose to offer an alternative, explanation or not, but in any event, begin to say no.

37. *Get organized* — your office, files, kitchen, closets, junk drawer . . . your life. You can find things easier and faster. Order results in less stress and does wonders for efficiently serving those depending on you.

38. *Be realistic when planning your time.* Plan, prioritize, and adjust. First, be sure to plan your day. If you don't have a plan, someone else will have one for you. Secondly, and this is really key, prioritize your list. You always want to be focused on what's most important at any given time (see tip #39). Third, make your best estimate of how long it will take for you to complete each item. Now here's another important key — multiply your best estimate by 1.5 and set aside that amount of time in your scheduling.

39. *Prioritize and stay focused.* Remember the Paretto Principle, better known as the 80/20 rule: i.e., 80 percent of your business comes from 20 percent of your efforts/customers. Focus on the important 20 percent. Don't forget to prioritize your priorities.

40. *Remove your name from miscellaneous mailing lists* and e-mail lists. Set aside the time to contact those catalog or other direct mail companies that constantly send you unsolicited information. Keep only the ones that bring value to you and are worth your precious time. Every minute is indeed precious. The time it takes to go through and sort and throw them away is time you could be spending on things or people who bring you joy. Also unsubscribe to some of the unsolicited e-mail you get. Seeing 10, 25, 50+ e-mails to review in your mailbox can be stressful in itself.

Know that you have what it takes to have more balance and less burnout in your life. It really comes down to a choice. Balance or burnout? Which do you choose?

ABOUT
CELESTE JONSON

*C*eleste Jonson is President and CEO of celeste jonson international inc., a human development and coaching company created to facilitate purposeful lifestyle development. She has 25 years of diverse business experience including media sales, marketing and management. For two years she worked with internationally known motivational speaker Les Brown. Together they presented keynotes and seminars across the U.S. Additionally, they co-hosted a weekly talk radio show in Chicago.

Celeste's training for the New York City Marathon opened her eyes to unique insight on how others can develop a winning spirit essential to becoming a champion in his or her own life. Celeste helps people discover new ways to restore balance, master change, expand thinking, communicate with power and maximize effectiveness as a leader. Through energizing keynotes, live training and educational resources, Celeste captures your attention, educates, encourages and inspires you to be your best.

Contact information:
Celeste Jonson
celeste jonson international inc.
200 North Pickett Street
Suite 1405
Alexandria, VA 22304
Phone: (703) 461-7955
Fax: (703) 461-7966
E-mail: jonsoninc@aol.com
Website: www.celestejonson.com

THE NEW GAME OF LIFE

by Dr. Patricia K. Tice

For this average, tea-drinking, semi-vegetarian, long-distance runner, the news was stunning: it is malignant. Interductal, metastatic breast cancer. It is the loneliest phrase in the world: "It is malignant." Gerry, my surgeon and my friend, looked deep into my eyes as he waited for my response. "Get it out of there," I heard myself saying, "Get it out of there as fast as you can. I have a garden to plant and a life to live."

I believe the only disability in existence is the disability of a bad attitude. Everything else is workable. And so began my year-long journey into the scary world of cancer and chemotherapy. It was April of 1999. Within two weeks I had had two surgeries. I put pen to paper and started to write. About faith, and hope and health. And I learned lessons along the way. The first piece I wrote was for Gerry, my surgeon.

Great Reasons for Having One Breast

1. I have never made money off two breasts; therefore, losing one will not make any difference.
2. Any pressure of trying to obtain cleavage is now gone.
3. Underwire bras will no longer dig into my skin.
4. When purchasing bras, one can obtain them at half price.
5. See-through tops are more interesting.
6. My gynecologist doesn't have to work as hard.

7. Mammograms are half price!

8. Having one breast raises the concept of "strapless gown" to a whole new level.

9. Less body powder.

10. You can keep your date in suspense. Only *you* know for sure.

— Dr. Patricia Tice, April 1999

Note: Patricia Tice underwent surgery for a single mastectomy on April 14, 1999. She is preparing to celebrate the end of chemotherapy treatments very soon. Bring on the band!

Gerry, in my first follow up after the surgery, said, "Take a deep breath and be brave. This will go fast." With that, he deftly and quickly pulled the bandage off my chest where my breast had been. The bandage was easily the size of half of my chest. I remember thinking about the size of the band-aids I had known as a child. This was the grown-up version.

I showed Gerry the "Ten Great Reasons for Having One Breast." He laughed so hard that he was forced to sit down. The "Ten Great Reasons . . ." are still posted on his examining room walls. As I look back on this writing, it is striking that I wrote, "She is preparing to celebrate the end of chemotherapy treatments very soon." I had not even started chemotherapy treatments at that time.

LESSON LEARNED: Always focus forward. If you look back, it will sink you.

Having been athletic all of my life, my body was not prepared for the effects of the chemotherapy. Each and every session made me violently ill. Every time my oncologist would say: "Most folks get along with this [medicine] very well," I could be almost guaranteed to have it *not* go well with my body. After I was able to sit up following the first chemotherapy, I fashioned a miniature scoreboard for myself. It featured "Home" and "Visitors." Under "Home" was written "Tice"; under "Visitors" was written "Cancer." That was just how I treated the cancer: as an intruder. An unwelcome intruder. I made small cards that numbered to sixteen. I was determined to win this game, and win it with a great attitude. I took the scoreboard with me to every checkup, every treatment session, and every test. My mantra became: I am a healthy person except for the cancer. Every time a test came out in my favor, or I recovered from the chemo session, it would be a point for me and not for the cancer. I focused on every cell in my body being filled with light. My goal was to make the game a shutout in my favor at 16-0.

LESSON LEARNED: Life is a fierce competition, a game. And the rules are not necessarily fair.

Dependent on a single income, I went to work one day and found out I had been fired. It was the day before my third chemotherapy session. It happened to be Independence Day weekend, 1999. My white count plummeted, and I nearly lost the battle. The nurses taught me how to give injections to myself in an effort to boost the white count. So, every morning at 6:00 a.m., instead of doing a five-mile run, I was giving myself a shot in the thigh. My mother, bless her, was with me for every chemotherapy session, doing all those motherly things that are so incredibly comforting: tucking me into bed at night, making me take the anti-nausea medicine on time, and placing her warm hand on my forehead while telling me that she loved me.

LESSON LEARNED: Spend time with your mother. No matter what your issues, or her issues, be with her. After all, without her, you would not be here.

Fourth of July weekend was no exception. Mother bundled me up, placed a bucket in the car in case I needed to vomit, grabbed my score-card, and off we went to the family farm for a respite.

My ten-year-old nephew, Stephen, was visiting from Ohio. He loved being at the farm in the summer time. Picnics, fishing, exploring in the woods — we had great fun! And the Fourth of July was his favorite time of all. He and his Dad, my brother, would drive a few short miles to another state to purchase fireworks. Stephen would make sure they purchased all of our favorites — snake coils and rockets and submarines and such. We had our very own personal fireworks show! But the summer of 1999 was different. His Aunty Patricia was very ill.

When Mother and I arrived at the farm, Stephen had all of his fireworks ordered from smallest to largest in the middle of the living room floor. He had all of our favorites identified: "This is Grandma's favorite, and this is Dad's favorite, and this is *your* favorite, Aunty!" He took me in with his giant, chocolate brown eyes. It was the first time he had seen me bald. My 125-pound frame had shrunk to 105 pounds. I asked him if he wanted to touch my bald head. Gently, he nodded his head yes. His small hand reached out to my head. It felt like a gift.

A short while later, yet another wave of nausea passed through my body. I felt the need to lie down. Stephen followed me into the bedroom. As he watched his Grandma tuck me in, he said simply, "You're not going to die, are you Aunty?"

The scorecard read 2-0.

LESSON LEARNED: One of the most precious gifts of all is the love of a child. It is the essence of life itself.

Later that same weekend, my anti-nausea medicine ran out. I had the same amount of medicine that had worked for the previous chemotherapy sessions. This time it was not enough. Without the medicine, I could not look up without feeling like I was falling backwards. My mother called the oncologist, who could not provide any other explanation for the extreme-beyond-belief nausea, except for the fact that I had lost my job, and the stress of that would take any normal person under, let alone someone who is undergoing treatment for cancer.

So, here we were in small town Iowa on a holiday weekend needing cancer medicine. No stores were open. My mother got on the telephone and made thirty-some calls around the area — every hospital, every doctor, every pharmacist that she could find in the telephone book. In my chemo stupor, I said a silent prayer. The search was complicated by the fact that the medicine I needed was relatively new and incredibly expensive. Finally, a small town pharmacist, reached at home, offered to go to his store and get the medicine for me. Would the patient be able to ride the thirty miles to the store?

It was the longest ride of my life. But somehow, we made it. An Independence Day carnival was going on in the town square. People were laughing. The Ferris wheel was turning. Children were eating cotton candy.

Mother and I were doing a covert drug run in a darkened pharmacy.

We entered the store. It felt eerie to enter a dark store. As we walked to the back of the store to meet the pharmacist, I noticed beautiful porcelain teapots and cups placed on shelves. It brought me comfort to see them. A hardened and faithful tea drinker, it had been weeks since I had been able to enjoy a good cup of tea. The metallic taste in my mouth from the chemotherapy made it impossible to enjoy anything. After looking at my identification papers, the pharmacist handed me the medicine. "Three tablets was all I had," he replied with a look of concern on his face. "I hope that will work." He handed me a small cup of water.

The pharmacist was one of the angels who helped to save my life. I found out later that he could have lost his license to practice pharmacy because he had sold me the medicine. He was unable to reach my regular pharmacist in the city because of the holiday weekend. It takes approval by the regular pharmacist in order to dispense medicine to a patient. It was one of my first direct demonstrations of the power of the love of the Infinite Kingdom. But not the last.

LESSON LEARNED: Angels can be found in the most unexpected of places, as long as we are willing to notice them.

The ride back to the ranch was much better. Stephen had placed my chair outdoors, next to Grandpa Tice's apple tree. "It's the best seat in the house," he said with a wide smile.

In all of my life, there will never be fireworks as wonderful as those were that night.

Back in the city, I began a job search. It felt like I was in a torture chamber, stretched on a device that pulls you in two different directions. When sitting in interviews, I would begin to perspire under my wig, then feel the need to vomit all over the interviewer's desk. The mastectomy scar would go tight, then begin to pull. I would work hard to maintain my professional composure, then at long last, get into my car and collapse. If there was anything that was harder than the cancer treatments, it was the job search. At least with the chemotherapy, I knew exactly what the program was — when the treatments were, how they would feel, and so on.

With the job search, it was never-ending. The door could not be closed. Day after day, letter after letter, I would begin the day with hope and send the letters with hope. The interviews would go well. I would open myself completely to the interviewer, then once I got home, feel as though it went wonderfully well. Then, BOOM! The infamous number ten envelope would arrive in the post box, containing the rejection words. I would fall back into the dungeon, wondering what went wrong, and knowing that I would never know. The extreme fatigue from the chemotherapy left me bone-tired exhausted. The job search nightmare made it feel ten times worse. Then the whole process would start again. More than 400 times it happened this way.

LESSON LEARNED: People are not always truthful.

Not because they are necessarily dishonest; rather, they do not want to hurt your feelings. Find it in your heart to forgive them, for they know not the damage they cause.

I looked at the scoreboard and concentrated on my healthy cells. My former husband and my former fiancée both ran the other way. They couldn't handle it.

LESSON LEARNED: Be grateful for the wishes that don't come true.

I learned quickly who the angels were in my life. I renewed my faith and became a truth student. I lost my home. I sold furniture to buy bread, milk, and crackers (to combat the nausea). As I met others who were dealing with similar things, I continued to write.

This creative writing piece was first written for the *Des Moines Register*. On May 3, 2000, I recorded it for National Public Radio at WOI studios in Ames, Iowa. Shortly after, it aired at the national level on "All Things Considered."

No-Hair Days

I don't have bad hair days . . . I have no hair days. So it was with interest that I read the recent article about the Yale University study regarding bad-hair days. Apparently it makes a person's self-esteem go down the tubes when their hair is out of place. And men suffer more than women do. Gentle listeners, please, let us check the reality. For this long-distance runner, semi-vegetarian, tea-drinker, the news was stunning: it is malignant.

Gosh, I wonder how people would handle it if their hair *went out of the place*. Meaning down the drain, in the waste can, all over the pillow, and so on. Every place except on your head or on your body. Then suddenly: no eyebrows, no eye-lashes (ouch, that hurts), no hair — anyplace. I was suddenly faced with weird decisions. Should I shampoo my bald head?

At first, it seemed like the worst. It was the worst! But, after experiencing the first few treatments of chemotherapy — what we lovingly refer to as "the red Kool-Aid," adminis-tered from syringes the size of nuclear warheads — suddenly, my fears vanished. Hair out of place? I just wanted hair! I did not care if people stared at my bald head. I was thrilled to be able to sit upright without feeling the need to vomit. Self-esteem, feeling capable and competent — gave way to a fight for life. Consequently, I established a new rule for my family: No complaints about hair allowed!

I have a new level of empathy for balding men. Forgive

me if I have no patience with people fussing over their hair, what it is or isn't doing, and how it makes them feel.

A few weeks ago, I used a comb for the first time in nearly a year. It was thrilling. Now that my eyebrows have returned, who knows, maybe I have a potential career as a model in San Francisco.

The humor helped to strengthen my resolve to beat the disease and make it a shutout on the scorecard. I purchased a tiara to use with other breast cancer patients to make them "queen for a day." It was a miraculous transformation to watch the effects of the tiara. It was truth in action.

LESSON LEARNED: Do something nice for someone else. Every day.

Even a small word or gesture. Even if they haven't earned it. Those are the people that need it most of all. It will pay you dividends that will last a lifetime.

At long last, it was nearing the end of the chemotherapy treatments. I had lost everything. Yet I had everything I needed. As I went in to talk with my oncologist just before that final session, I looked back at the waiting room. It was filled with people going through battles similar to mine. Many of them looked pale, anemic, and gaunt — there were no smiles. They had embraced "the chemo look." I thought about my journey. I thought about the four things. The four things that everyone in the world wants, no matter who they are:

- Something to learn,
- Something to look forward to,
- Something to hope for, and
- Someone to love.

I asked my oncologist if I looked like everyone in the waiting room. "No," he replied. "What's the difference?" I asked. "They are going through a similar treatment that I am."

"That's right," he said. "They are. The difference with you is your attitude and your faith. And that's why you're beating this disease."

LESSON LEARNED: Thank your doctors and nurses. They are doing God's work, unselfishly and miraculously.

For the final chemotherapy session, I dressed to the hilt. If you are taking chemo, make the best of it! My prettiest pearls, glamorous rings on each finger, a beautiful skirt. A limousine drove me to and from the session. My mother and aunt planned a grand party for me at the hospital. We had pizza and birthday cake — it wasn't my real birthday, but rather, a new birthday! As the nurses were inserting the needles, I was serenaded by an a cappella quartet singing "The Chemo Jive." A grand time was had by all! I arrived home to find my house decorated with dozens of pink balloons. The score was 15-0.

I had all four things: I had learned new lessons. I had learned about Truth. And Hope. And Health. And the greatest of all was the Love that made it possible.

At long last, the darkness began to lighten. Unless we say yes to life, the human spirit cannot triumph. Living halfway is not living at all. It is like having a lukewarm faith. Thank goodness, God gave us a strong survival instinct, a life force that resists to the end. Perhaps the mystery is why it sometimes takes a life-threatening illness to bring us to this truth. Life is absolutely precious. Each and every piece of it.

At the millennium New Year's Eve Gala a few weeks later, I was celebrating the completion of chemotherapy treatments. My new hair was one sixteenth of an inch long. No eyelashes yet. No eyebrows yet. Yet I was determined to look and feel as glamorous as all of the two-breasted women at the ball. I became Cinderella with one breast for that night. I designed a strapless gown that would properly cover the mastectomy scar. Everyone wanted to know where I got my gorgeous gown! One young man, upon seeing me enter the ball room, approached me, and proclaimed that he thought me "the most beautiful woman he had ever seen." Success! He was young enough to be my son. This average person felt like a queen. And the score was 16-0.

Want to know how you are doing at The New Game of Life? Get yourself a nice cup of tea, and do the following checklist:

Your New Game of Life Checklist
Rules to Live By

1. Do you currently have something to look forward to?
   ☐ Yes   ☐ No

2. Have you been able to forgive yourself for past mistakes you have made?
   ☐ Yes   ☐ No

3. Do you regularly try to do something for someone else?
   ☐ Yes   ☐ No

4. During the week, do you do something for yourself?
   ☐ Yes   ☐ No

5. Do you have something new to learn?
   ☐ Yes   ☐ No

6. Do you have something to hope for?
   ☐ Yes   ☐ No

7. Do you do a physical exercise on a regular basis?
   ☐ Yes   ☐ No

8. Do you do a mental exercise several times a week?
   ☐ Yes   ☐ No

9. On a regular basis, do you do a prayer that includes counting your blessings?
   ☐ Yes   ☐ No

10. Do you have someone or something to love?
    ☐ Yes   ☐ No

KEY: Each 'Rule' is worth ten points for a "Yes." A "No" is worth zero points.

80-100 — You are finding meaning in your life. Bravo.

50-80 — You need to see more meaning in your life. Where are your unfinished needs?

0-50 — Think about it. Where did you come from? What are you here for? Where are you going?

ABOUT
DR. PATRICIA K. TICE

*C*all on Patricia K. Tice to learn how to play The New Game of Life! *Patricia grew up in rural Iowa among the tall corn stalks of her father's farm. All of her life she has traveled the unused path. Having been told she was "not college material," she determinedly went on to earn a doctorate at the world's pre-eminent university, Oxford. Told she could not write well enough to complete a graduate degree, Dr. Tice has corresponded with The Princess of Wales, been published in* Coping, *the national magazine of the National Cancer Survivors Foundation, and her essays have aired on National Public Radio's* All Things Considered. *Her* The New Game of Life *talks were born from her near death experience with breast cancer.*

A shameless tea drinker (Patricia has taken tea with Sir Paul McCartney), she is affectionately called The Tea Doctor. *Her* Tea & Truth *series of lectures has received glowing reviews. People remark on her caring attitude and magical way of connecting. She is an engaging, thought-provoking and practical speaker.*

Contact Information:
Dr. Patricia Tice
The Tea Doctor
4861 Park Drive
West Des Moines, IA 50265-5330
Phone: (515) 457-7590
E-mail: pktice@home.com
Website: www.TheTeaDoctor.com

REBOUNDING FROM BURN-OUT TO BALANCE
(The Confessions of a Recovering Aerobics Instructor)

by Bonnie Dean

"Do not let your fire go out, spark by irreplaceable spark,
in the hopeless swamps of the approximate,
the not-quite, the not-yet, the not-at-all.
Do not let the hero in your soul perish in the lonely frustration
for the life you deserved, but have not been able to reach.
Check your road and the nature of your battle.
The world you desire can be won.
It exists, it is real, it is possible, it is yours."

— Ayn Rand

In the November/December 2000 issue of *Life @ Work* magazine, a magazine that blends Biblical wisdom and marketplace excellence, I found the best definition of balance: *Balance — the ability to continually recognize and juggle the multidimensional assignments and opportunities of life*. Wow! The challenge is identifying the assignments and recognizing the opportunities.

The May 2000 *Asian Wall Street Journal* reported the number of people working 60 hours a week in the United States had hit its highest peak in 20 years. In 1999 *Forbes* reported that in 60 percent of marriages both partners are working (up from 44 percent in the late '60s).

The balance of work and family is the top challenge stressing out our population according to most major work-related surveys. We are being driven crazy by technology. We suffer from over-communication. Cell phones and pagers constantly hound us. We are being asked to do more with less. Encouragement and support are an afterthought. No wonder so many of us are feeling burned out and out of balance.

It is easy to be out of balance today because our energy focus is constantly changing. We zoom past childhood, careers, marriage, family changes, forced career moves, our bodies changing and letting us down, taking care of aging parents, and staring at our own retirement choices. Where on that road were the rest stops? Were we all going so fast that we missed the off-ramps that help create the balance in our journey? Is it ever too late to choose another route?

Three days ago the alarm jolted me from a deep sleep at 6 a.m. Falling out of bed into my sweats and tennis shoes, I grabbed the leash, water bottles, car keys, and Charlie. We headed to the park for our eight-mile walk as the DJ on the radio announced that today was "National Stress Day!" This doesn't come as a big surprise. (Like we need a designated day to remind us!) Last year on this same date, the *Los Angeles Times* ran a full-page story on the latest badge being earned by Girl Scouts to add to their sash, *a stress management badge!* I don't remember thinking that I had to handle stress when I was twelve years old, do you?

However I have felt I've been on the *fast track* for the last twenty years. Six years ago, on this same day, an event occurred that shifted the stress gears in my life and put me on a different road to day-to-day balance. How was it, you ask that I can remember this date so accurately? It's my birthday and has been for fifty-one years. Before I go forward with this story, let me take you back.

Over the last 30 years I have been a college student, an aerobics instructor, marathon runner, Kauai backpack guide, wife, divorcee, stepmom, commissioned salesperson, sales trainer, and professional speaker. Each of these career choices has been accompanied by its own unique type of stress, but none has thrown my life so off-balance and into personal burnout than being a speaker.

From the beginning the stress came from fear, pulverizing, paralyzing, sweat-dripping-down-your back fear. Fear — that nagging feeling that wakes you up at four in the morning and won't let you fall back into a peaceful sleep. But like most things in life, the more you work through the things you are afraid of, the easier they get and the stress factors fall away. By year two my career started propelling me forward at the speed of light. I got so involved in "me" that I lost sight of my spiritual life. I had my family hanging onto my coattails. I had little time for friends, hobbies, and health. That thing known as balance was way out of whack in my life. Everything I did during this time frame reminds me now of the way I once taught aerobics — full bore, knee to nose, no pain, no gain. My family never complained . . . but letters stopped coming since the last ones hadn't been answered. My husband would come home from work and was left to entertain himself since I was always locked up in my office wheeling and dealing. The over-all tone from family was "don't bother with family affairs; we know you are too busy!" My life was out-of-balance headed for the danger zone.

Six years ago on April 19, 1995, I was speaking on a cruise ship sailing through the Panama Canal with a final destination of New York City. An announcement came over the PA system that knocked the wind out my sails. That was the day of the Oklahoma City bombing; a day that changed lives forever. Stop and think about how many people went to work that day angry with himself or herself or someone they loved. It was a day when husbands lost wives, children lost parents, sisters lost brothers. Friends and lovers were never going to get another opportunity to say to people they loved, "I'm sorry," "I was wrong," "forgive me," or "I love you."

That was the day many of us realized two of the saddest words in any language are "*what if?*" *What if* I had spent more time with my kids, grandkids, Godchildren? *What if* I had been a better partner? *What if* I had made better choices? *What if* I hadn't let my job control my life? *What if* I had slowed down to focus on what was really important in my life?

Focus on what's really valuable to you

How easy is it to focus on what has real value in our lives? Gloria Steinem once said that if you want to know what's really important to you, pull out your checkbook and your day timer. Right now, get out four separate pieces of paper. On each write one of the four things that you value most in your life. For some it might be your spiritual life, your health, your financial freedom, or your family. There are no right or wrong answers here, only the four things that you value most in your life. Did I say four, oops, accounting error; I meant the three most important things in your life. Throw one away — sorry. Now you hold in your hands the three things you value most in your life. What if something happened and you could only keep two of them? Which would you most easily give up? Crumple up one more of your values and toss it out right now. In your hands you've got the two things you value most in life.

What do they mean to you? What are you thinking . . . that I'm now going to ask you to narrow your choices down to one? Thanks for the inspiration. Please throw away one more value leaving you with the *one thing* you value most in life. Take a minute and think about what that remaining thing means to you and how you would feel without it in your life. Now finally, throw that last value on the floor and step on it. How do you feel? Empty? Alone? I played the bad guy here asking you to throw away the things you value most in life, to crumple them up and step on them. I believe, on a daily basis, most of us do this to ourselves by constantly reacting to urgent demands at the expense of important demands. We put on the back burner the things we value most in our lives!

Focus on the little things done well

The way to slowly start turning this focus around is all rice and potatoes. To quote that well-known philosopher Flip Wilson, "What you see is what you get." Have you ever noticed what we focus on in life tends to expand? Studies show we get interrupted approximately every eight minutes all day long. With all those interruptions it's no wonder we constantly work on *urgent* issues (the rice), instead of focusing on *important* ones (the potatoes).

Imagine a clear glass container on the table in front of you. Think of all the things you fill your time with. Imagine these *urgent* assignments as grains of rice filling that glass container more than two-thirds to the top. In a panic, on a daily basis, we attempt to put the potatoes, the things we value most, somewhere into the day and they spill over the top onto the floor. *What if* we began each day with a clear container and put the potatoes, the things we value most, first? *What if* we put things like family, health, and our spiritual life in first? Would there still be room for the rice? *Yes.* Watch as we place the little red potatoes in the glass container. Now we pour the rice in and are amazed as the grains trickle down in and around the potatoes and fill the container to the brim. Things fall into place better this way. With a different focus and a little preplanning, not only is there room for *urgent* and *important* in our jar, there is still room for a cup or two of water (opportunities) which we are now pouring through the rice and potatoes into our lives. The next time you are trying to juggle your daughter's dance recital and working late, think about rice and potatoes.

Just do a little . . . a lot

Owning my own business, being a wife, mother, grandmother, Godmother, daughter, community volunteer, president of any organization I ever belonged to, athlete, overachiever and type A personality, I operated in the burnout mode for too many years. Here are 16 balance ideas I've collected and put into use that have opened my heart and soul to the opportunities around me daily to bring more calm into my hectic life.

16 Ways to Rebound

1. Master the Moment

No matter what you are doing, from brushing your teeth to making a cup of steaming hot coffee, from driving to work to driving that putt — be present in that moment and enjoy it! When you're at work . . . be there! When you leave work . . . leave it! Having my own business, which comes with the handicap of a home office, I have learned to leave my office at

5:30 and close the door. I do not answer my office phone in the evenings as I used to do on a regular burnout basis. In the last six years there has been nothing, not one thing, that couldn't wait until the next morning.

Many of you come home at night and are exhausted, looking forward to sitting down with your feet up reading the paper or in a hurry to get dinner on the table. The moment you open the door your kids are clamoring for your valuable time and attention. Instead of putting them off with promises of later, practice the *"ninety second potato"* ritual. Give your children one-and-a-half minutes of your undivided, direct eye contact, turn-off-all-internal-tapes attention. Focus the moment on them, their needs, their excitement, and their story. Most often, ninety seconds will satisfy the moment. Then they can move on to their chores for the evening and you to yours. Try this ninety-second technique at work too.

2. Protect Your Emotional Immune System (EIS)

I first learned of the EIS from C. Leslie Charles in her book, *Why Is Everyone So Cranky?* The phrase, emotional immune system, made absolute sense to me. It is our internal compass that charts our direction. Our EIS is what alerts us we're headed for burnout and need to switch course and steer in a different direction. Our emotional immune systems need a shot of vitamin B-12 everyday. The complexity of the choices we face each day either builds them up or tears them down. Let's explore a few ways to protect our emotional immune systems.

Pick your battles.

Do you have teenagers in your house or encounter difficult situations at work? Do you find you have a short fuse and react without thinking and your entire day becomes infected by mental madness, that cranky chatter in your own mind that replays the event over and over and stars you as the bad guy? How important in the scope of a lifetime are most of these issues? It's time to start stepping outside ourselves, mastering the moment, *responding* instead of *reacting* and making better choices for our EIS. If your teenager has a messy room — close the door. If someone is violent at work — call the police. If you get stuck in traffic on your way to an appointment — call ahead on your cell-phone, take a deep breath, relax, and sing along with your favorite CD. Decide which events are life threatening, which are things that shall come to pass, and which are out of your control and then respond accordingly. We get so invested in the control issues of battles, which are all but forgotten in a few weeks time but have put a divot in our EIS. Choose to boost your EIS instead of bursting it.

Influence vs. Control

I have a sign on my desk that says "the only thing you can control is how you respond to the stress in your day-to-day life." I start each day with a brief focus and a prayer as I read that sign. A major lesson I have learned over the six-year journey from burnout to better life balance is that we don't have much control in the lives of others around us . . . but we do have influence. I am an admitted control freak. It has been a hard lesson. The only real control we have is how we *respond* to the daily stress in our own lives. We influence the lives of those around us by our responses/reactions to that stress, period. These responses greatly affect our EIS and how we feel about ourselves. Are you happy with your responses to the stressful situations in your life? I can admit here that I teach what I most need to learn. It is a never-ending battle with myself, but one worth working on. It's not about resigning; it's about surrendering to a greater cause — you! I practice relaxing and surrendering to a place of emotional well-being.

L.A.R.P.

We all have four basic needs to keep ourselves in balance. We master the moments best when we provide these basics to the people we work, play, and live with.

Listened to — One of the greatest gifts we can give to each other is undivided attention.

Acknowledged — You don't have to always agree with people, but it's important to let them know you heard what they had to say.

Respected — We teach people how to treat us by the way we treat others. If you want to know the values of another person, watch how they treat people who serve them.

Praised — Do you know anyone who suffers from too much recognition and praise? Don Peterson, the former CEO of Ford believes the most important time of the day is the time spent boosting the morale of the people around you. I agree.

3. Simplify — *Learn to let go of all the guilt and worry and clutter in your life.*

Learn to say NO and not feel guilty. Time has become the currency of this new millennium. Protect your time. Invest it well. So often we let our mouths overload our backs by saying *yes* to things we should have said *no* to in the first place. When we overschedule ourselves with obligations and events we really don't care about, we start to feel angry, upset, and resentful. When someone asks you to spend time on an activity you don't want to do, say, "Thank-you for thinking of me. I am already booked that evening." You may be booked sitting at home reading a good book or spending the day working in the yard with your family. Take responsibility for your own potatoes . . . it's healthy!

Learn to let your phone ring.

We forget that the telephone is a convenience, not an assignment. There are times when it is ok to just let the phone ring. I remember the first time my husband David and I were having dinner and I didn't answer the phone. He looked up startled and asked, "Aren't you going to answer that?" "No," I replied, "I'm having dinner with you. The message center will pick up the call, and I can return it after we're done." When did we get so locked into this high-tech phone world that we misplaced the high touch of reaching out and talking to the people across the table?

Give your television the night off.

Here's a challenge to all of you die-hard, four-hour-a-night TV buffs . . . turn the tube off one night a week and have a family night. Get out the board games, have a crafts night, cook up tempting treats in the kitchen, go to the beach and watch the sunset . . . anything but another mindless-talkless evening. We talk about not having enough time, yet most televisions are on 20-40 hours a week. Hummmmmmmmm.

Get rid of excess clutter.

We live in a consumer age. The home storage business is at an all-time high because we cling to our "stuff." It's amazing the amount of damage crammed closets and overstuffed offices, garages, and cupboards can do to our emotional well-being.

Recently, I got rid of all my old, clunky office furniture. My office had become so overcrowded I hated to go into it and it was with anxiety when I did. The new office was created with mission style furniture, a writing table with no drawers to collect clutter, and a computer table behind me to clear my working desk space. Now, time in my open spaced office is inviting and productive. Room by room, closet by closet I am working my way through the house and garage — *slowly* — giving things to Goodwill, a family member, or unloading at a neighborhood garage sale.

Clear the clutter from your mind.

We carry around other kinds of clutter— mental clutter. I heard a story years ago about a man who had a large family and was struggling to make ends meet. When he came home at night, he appeared happy and worry-free even though he carried the weight of the world on his shoulders. When asked his secret, his state of grace, he replied that he had a big oak tree in front of his house that was older than his grandfather. He called it his "worry tree." When he came home at night he hung all his worries on that tree, no sense dragging them into the house where they could bother him and take his mind off his family. The worries would still be hanging there in the morning if he chose to pick them up and take them back to work.

Try keeping a "hang loose" journal next to your bed.

Before you go to sleep at night write down the things that are causing you stress or making you feel out of balance. Let go of them for the night. Turn them over to a higher power and get a good night's rest.

4. Make Healthy Choices

The years I taught aerobics I thought I was making healthy choices, but, in retrospect, I think it only worked because I had youth on my side. I believed that food was meant to be eaten in the car, on the run, over the sink, or while rushing from one activity to the next. Obvious choices for this venue of consumption were fast food outlets, fried, greasy food that saps our energy and slows down our response systems. As we get older (and wiser) we discover our bodies are less forgiving. I have learned a great deal about healthy choices from Dr. Edward A. Taub on PBS and from his book, *Balance Your Body, Balance Your Life*.

He has a lot to say on how to increase energy and well-being in your life by climbing the 12-step food energy ladder to better health. We can't keep putting poor fuel into our bodies and expect to get healthy results. The same is true for the proper amount of sleep you permit yourself. We are able to respond better to the challenges in our daily schedules, at home and at work, with a good night's rest.

For the serious student of better choices, consider having a licensed dietician come to your home and go through your cupboards and refrigerator with you to really understand the quality of the choices you've been making.

The Dreaded "E" Word

For two decades I was a runner, injuries turned me into a walker, and now swimming is the best, low-pact cardiovascular exercise I can get. People tell me they are too tired to exercise. The truth is they are too tired because they are not exercising. If you can't "red ink" in 30-40 minutes for yourself three to four times a week to exercise, *there is a problem*. We find time for the things we really want to do. Get out of bed a half hour earlier than usual and start walking for twenty minutes before you shower and go to work. I promise within the first two weeks of adding this activity to your busy schedule you will feel better, have more energy, and have more patience with yourself and others.

Try walking for 20 minutes before you go to bed at night. Drag yourself away from the television and you will find you sleep better, your food will digest better, and your mind will be much more alert the following day at work. Start making an appointment with yourself in red ink to show it is a priority and non-negotiable.

5. Take "Time Outs"

"For fast acting relief . . . try slowing down!" — Lily Tomlin

While you have that calendar out, ink in "time-out" days for yourself for the rest of the year. These are days when you get a chance to slow down and refill your spirit and soul. Remember the hokey pokey we all danced to as children? You put your whole self in — you take your whole self out. If you're like me, and I know I certainly am, you put your whole self in until you fall into bed at night. Once a month our balance depends on permitting ourselves time-outs. Take your whole self to a museum or on a picnic in the park, work in your garden, walk on the beach with a friend or in quiet solitude. We don't spend enough quality alone time to refill ourselves. Taking our whole self out occasionally gives us better balance when we put our whole selves back in. You return to work refreshed, renewed, and recharged!

6. Develop Your Seventh Sense

Learn to find the humor in day-to-day situations. What we can laugh through we can live through. Laughter is one of the best medicines for your emotional immune system! Learn to laugh at yourself and aid others in laughing along with you. Invest in clown noses. (Available at teacher supply stores or call 1-800-228-2269.) Give them to your friends and family. Whether we are stuck in traffic, delayed at airports, confronted by an explosive situation or dealing with life's challenges, we can choose to live in frustration or fascination. Don your clown nose in times that once stressed you and start fascinating yourself. You'll find it is hard to be upset.

7. Nurture with Nature

From South Africa to Lake of the Ozarks, Missouri, I have asked audience members what they do to maintain balance in their lives. The answer I most frequently get is "work in my garden." Most of the responses have to do with getting out in nature and slowing down our pace. Many people include their pets in their nature quests or merely spend time with their pets at home. I have found nature to be very kind when I need to be nurtured. It is amazing what a 15-minute walk in the park can do for stimulating both sides of your brain and renewing energy for the second half of your day.

8. Feng Shui

Another book that has helped me create a harmonious environment to nurture and calm my home and office is *Sacred Space* by Denise Linn. Her latest book is *Feng Shui for the Soul*. If this is a science you are not familiar with, I encourage you to pick up one of her books and expand your knowledge in this area.

9. ASK!

It says in the Bible, "Ask and ye shall receive." If God didn't want us to ask he wouldn't have put it in the book! Learn to ask for what you need from the people you work with and especially your family. Our expectations often get us into stressful situations. We rarely let the other person know what our expectations are, and then we are disappointed or angered when these expectations are not met. If you have people working for you, teach them to ask for what they need to do their jobs better and bring out the best of themselves in the effort.

10. Reward Yourself

Behavior that is rewarded will be repeated is the number one rule of management. Wouldn't it make sense to reward yourself for behavior you want to continue. When you have completed the task you hate to do, influenced a situation, or helped others laugh at a problem and move on . . . reward yourself. Take yourself to lunch, plant an herb garden in a container to make your office smell great, get yourself some fresh cut flowers or scented candles for your home or office, or pick up a treat for the family on the way home. One of my favorite rewards is a full body massage.

11. Be Kind to Yourself

Enough said. No one beats us up the way we beat up ourselves. Take a class at a local college. Tai chi, yoga, longevity stick, and wellness classes, they all teach you to be kinder to yourself.

12. The Power of the Personal Note

A challenge I give every one of my audiences is to write one personal note a day. E-mail does not count. Take the challenge and send a handwritten note of thank-you or just to stay in touch and see how that affects your year. Five notes a week times four is twenty notes a month; times twelve is two hundred forty handwritten notes a year. I guarantee it will change the life of your business and the business of your life.

13. Positive Support Team

There are two kinds of people on this planet, *mentors and tormentors.* Surround yourself with a positive support team. Life is full of toxic energy drainers. Avoid them. Spend your time with people who are like-minded and striving for more balance in their lives, too. Hold each other accountable for the goals you've set for yourselves in these areas. My PST calls me to walk, get a massage, or take a wellness class. We encourage each other to take steps to eat better, read more, relax more, play more. Years ago we stopped giving each other gifts and started giving each other memories. Spa days, concerts under the stars, cooking classes, yoga classes, and outings to see desert flowers and migrating birds are ways we celebrate birthdays and anniversaries now. I cherish my friends who don't let me give them excuses for not having better balance in my life.

14. Drink Lots (of Water)

It cleans the impurities out of our systems and keeps all the juices flowing and internal organs working well.

15. Footnote

All of the above suggestions have played an active part in maintaining some semblance of balance in my crazy life. After the

Oklahoma City bombing I focused on the priorities in order of value in my life. I put my family and my spiritual life before my career and everything began falling into better balance immediately. These past six months I have been knocked off balance repeatedly. My husband, David, had a long awaited hip replacement surgery, and I was his home health care nurse for six weeks. We spent ten hours in the emergency room in December with the threat of a heart attack that was later diagnosed as pleurisy. The following day we had 19 people at our home to celebrate the holidays. (I had a lot of help!) Earlier this year my 77-year-old mother was diagnosed with lung cancer, had part of her lung removed, and will be moving in with us for a 4-6 week rehab. We did cancel our three-week speaking tour in Africa this fall. Something had to give, and we are working on moving the dates to next year. June will see us in Madison, Wisconsin, celebrating our Godchild Katey's high school graduation. This July we will be hosting a "20-40-60" party to celebrate our granddaughter turning 20, our oldest turning 40, and my husband reaching 60 all in the same month! All this while running a thriving speaking business, supplying the neighbors with plenty of fresh vegetables from my garden, training for and participating in a 60-mile breast cancer awareness three-day fund raising walk, and enjoying it all as I strive to practice what I teach. I share this because not long ago *I would have missed out* on many of these events. After April 19, 1995 my priorities changed. When Katey used to come to visit for two weeks every summer, I wondered how I could "fit her in." What a blessing the last six summers have been. I have "fit in" my speaking around her visits.

Katey will graduate from high school only once, and we thank God every day that she wants us to be a part of it. Our family is now spread out all over this country, and thank God they want to spend their valuable vacation time with us. Life is short. The rice will always be there; the potatoes are what slip away. The burnout is much less and the balance is getting better.

16. Rebounding Takes Time

They say give a busy person something else to do and he or she will get it done. Here are a few opportunities to take on that road from burnout to balance. We can't make time; we have to take time for what we need.

Take time to think; it is the source of power.
Take time to read; it is the foundation of wisdom.
Take time to play; it is the secret of staying young.
Take time to be quiet; it is the opportunity to seek God.
Take time to be aware; it is the opportunity to help others.
Take time to love and be loved; it is God's greatest gift.
Take time to laugh; it is the music of the soul.
Take time to be friendly; it is the road to happiness.
Take time to dream; it is what the future is made of.
Take time to pray; it is the greatest power on earth.

— Author Unknown

"This is the beginning of a new day. You have been given this day to use as you will. You can waste it or use it for good. What you do today is important because you are exchanging a day of your life for it. When tomorrow comes, this day will be done forever: in its place is something that you have left behind . . . let it be something you value."

ABOUT
BONNIE DEAN

*B*onnie Dean is fun. *Her trademark is her glitzy tennis shoes, which symbolize her enthusiasm, high energy and camaraderie with her audiences. Bonnie is known internationally as* The Motion Coach *for getting people up and off their assets. She has been a recent guest on* Cape Town Talk *in Johannesburg and* Women Talk *in Durban.*

Bonnie works with organizations that want to open channels of communication between internal and external customers, and individuals who want to learn simple tools that can make a difference in the lives of their business and the business of their lives. "Her gift is she takes common sense tools and gets uncommon results!" wrote a corporate meeting planner at Boeing. As a speaker and author, Bonnie teaches value-based communication skills and team building through creativity and fun. When you see her on stage, you'll see that her interactive teaching style and understated sense of humor create a stimulating learning environment.

Bonnie is the CCO (Chief Creativity Officer) of W.O.W. Presentations. Some her clients include Bank of America, Boeing North America, Canadian Airlines, Crystal Cruise Lines, Ford Motor Company, The Institute of Internal Auditors, Pacific Bell, State Farm Insurance, Toyota, Xerox and Yankee Dental Congress.

Contact information:
Bonnie Dean
W.O.W. Presentations
11823 Purslane Circle
Fountain Valley, CA 92708
Phone: (714) 531-7035
Phone: (800) 915-4668
Fax: (714) 531-1903
E-mail: bon4motion@aol.com
Website: www.BonnieDean.com

KEEPING STRESS FROM BECOMING DISTRESS

by Stephen K. Siemens, CSP

The age of the half-read page
And the quick hash and the mad dash,
The bright night and the nerves tight,
The plane hop, the brief stop,
The brain strain and the heart pain.
The cat naps till the spring snaps,
And the fun's done.

Do these words send up a red flag? Can anyone relate? While the author of the above poem is unknown, the lifestyle it describes is well known to many people. The surveys and statistics are alarming and revealing. More than 75 percent of all visits to primary care physicians are for stress-related complaints or disorders. Stress is responsible for more than half of the 550 million workdays lost annually to absenteeism. Forty-three percent of all adults suffer adverse health effects because of stress. The list goes on. In his book *Self-Talk*, David Stoop says that 40 million Americans suffer from allergies; 30 million suffer from sleeplessness; 25 million suffer from hypertension; 20 million suffer from ulcers — all a result of stress. According to medical research, 75 to 90 percent of all illnesses are caused by the stresses of modern life, or more specifically, by our responses to these stresses.

The fact is all of us have stress in our lives. Another fact is that stress can be both positive and negative. But here is the most important fact: most stress is unnecessary. And that means we don't have to live stressed out.

To keep stress from becoming distress, we must keep the proper perspective. Keeping the right perspective means being able to see what we are doing today as it fits into the big picture of life. When we lose our perspective about anything or anyone, we will change the way we view things or people. Whether we see something as a burden or a blessing is based on one word: perspective.

The following is a letter a girl sent her parents from college. It puts everything in, well, just read it and you'll understand.

Dear Mother and Dad,

Since I left for college, I have been remiss in writing and I am sorry for my thoughtlessness in not having written before. I will bring you up to date now, but before you read on, please sit down. You are not to read any further unless you are sitting down. Okay?

Well, then, I am getting along pretty well now. The skull fracture and the concussion I got when I jumped out of the window of my dormitory when it caught on fire shortly after my arrival here are pretty well healed now. I only spent two weeks in the hospital and now I can see almost normally and only get those sick headaches once a day. Fortunately, the fire in the dormitory, and my jump, were witnessed by an attendant at the gas station near the dorm and he was the one who called the fire department and the ambulance. He also visited me in the hospital, and since I had nowhere to live because of the burnt-out dormitory, he was kind enough to invite me to share his apartment with him. It's really a basement room but it's kind of cute. He is a very fine boy and we have fallen deeply in love and are planning to get married. We haven't got the exact date yet, but it will be before my pregnancy begins to show.

Yes, Mother and Dad, I am pregnant. I know how much you are looking forward to being grandparents, and I know you will welcome the baby and give it the same love and devotion and tender care you gave me when I was a child. The reason for the delay in our marriage is that my boyfriend has a minor infection, which prevents us from passing our pre-marital blood tests, and I carelessly caught it from him.

I know that you will welcome him into our family with open arms. He is kind, and although not well educated, he is ambitious. Although he is of a different race and religion than ours, I know your often-expressed tolerance will not permit you to be bothered by that.

Now that I have brought you up to date, I want to tell you that there was no dormitory fire, I did not have a concussion or skull fracture, I was not in the hospital, I am not pregnant, I am not engaged, I am not infected, and there is no boyfriend in my life. However, I am getting an F in history and an F in science, and I want you to see those grades in their proper perspective.

Your loving daughter,
Susie

So to give stress a rest, we must keep everything in perspective. Let's look at 11 practical steps that will help us keep stress from becoming distress.

Stay in the areas of your strengths. Nothing reveals your strengths like stress. When you "rise to the occasion" in a stressful situation, you often discover or are reminded of your areas of strength. However, when you fall short during stressful times, you can end up labeling areas of your life as weaknesses. Did you say "weaknesses"? Let me challenge that thought.

Begin by understanding that you have no weaknesses. What you really have are "undeveloped strengths." When you face life with this perspective or with this philosophy, you will be more productive and less stressed. Gain the perspective that all areas of your life are simply strengths or "undeveloped strengths." Venture into those areas that threaten you because they are nothing more than opportunities to grow and change. New opportunities and a new perspective will help you realize that you'll always be able to stay in the areas of your strengths.

Turn off the road of overload. I grew up on a farm and my Dad would stand in the middle of his field and say, "I don't go to work, I'm surrounded by it!" Most people today feel "surrounded." They have not learned to prioritize and to be intentional about giving up the good things for the *best* things. Organizing our time so that we can focus on the best things will involve saying "no" to other demands. Remember that saying "no" is okay and even necessary at times. However, it's a learned behavior that does not come easily to everyone. Determine your "yes's" and "no's" in light of your priorities and your personal mission statement. I probably can't prove this, but I don't think any birds ever tried to build more nests than other birds, any chipmunk ever died of anxiety because he didn't have enough corn for two winters, or any wolf lost its perspective because he had only one hole to hide in. Solid priorities and saying "no" when appropriate will ease our stress load. Become an "animal" in your commitment to keep a good life map in your mind, and turn off the road leading to overload.

Relationships matter. With whom we choose to spend our time is so important. Relationships really matter! We do become like the people we spend time with; that is why I'm careful and purposeful about spending my leisure time with positive people. One of my core values is to be negative-free, so I don't walk away from negative people, I run as fast as I can. For me, being around people who are positive and focused on helping others is very important. Here is a poem that I refer to often:

"There are two kinds of people on earth today,
Just two kinds of people, no more, I say.
Not the good and the bad, for 'tis well understood
That the good are half-bad and the bad half-good.
No! the two kinds of people on earth I mean
Are the people who lift and the people who lean."

—Ella Wheeler Wilcox

We need people who lift. People who care enough about us to be honest; who love us enough to still love when we are unlovely; who see us the same at our worst and best; who offer wise counsel and help keep our focus moving forward; who remind us we truly have purpose and potential. Relationships do matter! The bottom line question is this, "Do you spend time with people who add 'static' or 'stability' to your life?" Get rid of the static and watch your stress levels decline because of the stability good relationships offer!

Exercise. I lead a busy life just like you. My days fill up quickly just like yours. I know it's difficult to find time. General George Patton once said, "An active mind cannot exist in an inactive body." In the whole scheme of things, the small amount of time invested in exercising pays big dividends like increased energy, more creativity, better quality of sleep, increased lean muscle mass, and decreased fat. Karen Boscaljon says in her book *Mental Pull-ups* that one pound of muscle burns 45 calories a day while one pound of fat burns only two calories a day. Exercise needs to become a part of our routine.

To make it a habit, try committing to a 45-day plan. Why? When you take a closer look at the word "habit," you'll find out why it is hard to change. Work on a "habit" for five days, take off the "H" and you still have "a bit." Give it five more days, so that on the tenth day you take off the "A," and you still are left with a "bit." Then decide to work on it five more days, and you'll wake up on the fifteenth day to discover you still have "it." You get the picture. It takes at least 30-45 days to change a habit, and most people today work 5,10, or 15 days on what they are trying to change, then get discouraged and quit. Commit to get fit by making a 45-day exercise calendar and placing a star on the days you exercise and an unhappy face on the days you don't. It's a simple visual, but it will help you stay committed and, in turn, give some stress a rest!

How does exercise help? Researchers are finding that exercise enables the brain to cope better with stress. Preliminary evidence suggests that physically active people have lower rates of anxiety and depression than sedentary people. This may be due to findings that the hormone norepinephrine is released during exercise, which helps the brain deal with stress more efficiently. But don't take their word for it; do your own research and see how you feel after getting into the wonderful habit of consistent exercise.

Stop running from risks. For many people, taking risks can be very stressful because they are afraid of failure. But the fact is, failure is an event, an event from which to learn. Henry Ford said, "Failure is the opportunity to begin again, more intelligently." When we make failure personal, it becomes a negative. However, when we make it a learning process, it can be a positive event in our life. The question is not "if" we will take a risk, but "what" risk we will take. Then the question is not what happens if we fail; it is what can we do to make this event a stepping stone, not a tombstone? When I was a kid, we lived in Missouri and there were land turtles all over the place. My brother and I would collect them, feed them and pretend they were our special pets. At the age of nine, while playing with these turtles, Dad told me, "Never forget to be like a turtle for the rest of your life. You will only make progress when you stick your neck out." When we stop running from risks and "stick our neck out," we start living life to its fullest.

Stretch or get a massage. Everyone can learn to stretch regardless of age, flexibility, or fitness level. Stretching is one of the five components of fitness (cardio-respiratory fitness, muscular strength, muscular endurance, and body composition are the other four) and, unfortunately, it gets overlooked most of the time. Stretching relaxes the mind and the body and should become a part of your daily life. Regular stretching reduces muscle tension and makes your body feel more relaxed, increases range of motion, promotes circulation, and it just plain feels good! To relieve stress, try stretching first thing in the morning, at work, and before and after exercise.

You can also get a massage. Toxins (harmful things we eat, breathe, smoke or drink) get into our system and lodge into the muscle bed. The blood flowing through the muscle is immediately restricted, and the muscle sends out lactic acid to try to break down the deposit. The acid builds on top of the toxin and forms what we call a knot. A massage pushes through the muscle beds, helping to flush out toxins from the body. A massage can also help circulate blood cells, which in turn helps the heart, stomach, lungs, and all organs of the body. This process adds to the prevention of unnecessary tension and stress. And who really needs an excuse to indulge in a massage anyway?

Acquire a fun way to release stress. Healthy people develop and discover fun ways to release negative stress. Run, read, walk, swim, visit a friend, go to a care facility, sing, make a phone call, take a mini vacation — these are just a few ideas. Just find a way to release the negative stress, but make it fun. While serving as a college president, I realized the faculty and staff were stressed to the limit on a particular issue. I knew that if we didn't release some of that negative stress, our next staff meeting would create even more stress. We started our meeting by going outside and giving each person four golf balls, a driver, and a target. Needless to say since the majority were not golfers, we had some great laughs, a productive meeting, and made good decisions on the issue that was stressing everyone out.

Here are some things that work for me. I take a piece of paper, mentally write down all of the stress, wad it up and then play basketball with the trash can and my paper "stress" ball. Just for the record, stress loses and I win! I may also write down whatever stress I'm dealing with, then bury the note in the fire pit located on our concrete patio. With it buried, it is gone and I leave it there. And when we have a fire in the pit, stress loses again! Need another idea? Write down what you are stressed about on paper, seal it in an envelope, address the letter to Santa Claus at the North Pole and mail it. Don't put a return address on the envelope or any name or address inside the letter. After the mail person picks it up, it's gone, not to be returned, just like the stuff you were worrying or stressed about! Remember, having a fun way to release stress is important. It doesn't have to cost you anything, or at the most, 34 cents! Just keep it fun! And when throwing your golf clubs, always throw them in the direction you are going.

Reprogram your mind. One of my favorite quotes is, "If you can't fight and you can't flee . . . flow." The author, Robert Eliot, understands the popular poster on the rules for stress: Rule #1, don't sweat the small stuff; Rule #2, it's all small stuff. We need to reprogram our minds in order to keep stressful situations in the proper perspective. Since we program our minds by what we read, see, hear, watch and think about, we can reprogram our minds by changing the input. What we let in needs to add value and validity to our lives. Everything else is clutter. You can say "I can do it" or you can say, "I can't do it"; either way, you're going to be right. Remember the lessons we can learn from the animals! They don't stress about the small stuff and neither should we.

Eat well. It is important to remember that how you eat counts too. A healthy diet is the single most important aspect of maintaining a healthy body. Easy to do? Easy to change? No! Busy lifestyles can send stress levels soaring, making it tempting to forget about a balanced diet by skipping meals or eating anything while on the go. Yet, when your body does not get the balance of nutrition that it needs, you may find yourself trying to do more with less energy.

What are some good foods to eat when stressed? Karen Collins, M.C., RD, suggests aiming for a combination of grain products (like bread and pasta) with vegetables and fruits, along with a modest amount of protein, at least three times a day. Try to avoid "comfort foods" that contain high amounts of fat and sugar.

Also, it's important to set aside time to eat meals. The 15 to 20 minutes it takes to put aside work and other distractions will be more than compensated with a noticeable energy boost. And while many people today may turn to vitamins to increase levels of energy, there is no evidence that emotional stress increases our need for vitamins.

So when the pressure in your life increases, simplify your eating routines to save time, but don't give up on the good nutrition that is key to helping you through stressful times. For example, buy your veggies and fruits cut and cleaned so you can grab them on the run. Plan your meals ahead and take advantage of the low-fat, complete freezer meals. Eating well and staying healthy is a key step to keeping stress from becoming distress.

Stand on strong convictions. Nothing produces stress quicker than not having strong convictions. You need clarity on the things in your life that you will not bend on, or you'll be driven by the winds. With strong convictions, you can speak, live, act and respond without negative stress. You don't merely respond to what others do, because you act according to your core values and convictions. Even under difficult situations, when you stand on strong convictions, you can say "no" when you need to, "yes" when you want to, pursue your cause, love other people, and follow your goals and dreams. When we keep our perspective based on our convictions, we will stand!

Turn your focus outward. The happiest people today live to help other people. I am reminded of two people in my life who demonstrate a right and wrong focus. The first person, who will remain nameless, talks about all of the things that are not being done for him, what other people owe him, what his children owe him, or what others ought to be doing for him. This person just drains you whenever you are with him. You get the picture. The other individual, because of some physical challenges, could decide to be negative. Instead he lives to help others, can't express appreciation enough, and adds value to people's lives daily. What's the difference? His focus! This second person is my Dad. Like him, I feel better when I get up in the morning committed to help someone else succeed. I have less stress when I'm counting my blessings, not my burdens. There's no magic formula to obtaining this kind of focus. Someday we will be judged by the way we lived our lives, not by our possessions; by what we gave, not what we kept; and how we invested in people. Turn your focus outward and you'll have a more enjoyable, productive life. Thanks, Dad, for your example!

Simply stated, to keep stress from becoming distress, just **(GIVE)** . . .

Stay in the areas of your strengths

Turn off the road of overload

Remember relationships matter

Exercise

Stop running from risks

Stretch or get a massage

Acquire a fun way to release stress

Reprogram your mind

Eat well

Stand on strong convictions

Turn your focus outward.

As you take these steps, you're likely to feel a greater sense of control, harmony, and balance in your life. In the long run, you'll end up being more effective and the journey will be more enjoyable, successful, and restful! Travel well, my friend!

ABOUT
STEPHEN SIEMENS, CSP

*S*teve Siemens, aka, The People Builder, *is founder and president of Siemens People Builders, an organization which helps people and organizations reach personal and professional excellence. With a background in education and administration, Steve delivers high impact programs that are entertaining, memorable and packed with a wealth of information. He delights over a hundred audiences around the world each year. His most requested programs are* Don't Die Until You're Dead!; If It Isn't Broken, Break It; Don't Work for a Living: P-L-A-Y! *and* Brainwaves of a Leader. *He is the author of* Push-ups for People: 30 People Building Exercises to Help You and Others! *His diverse client list includes The Principal Financial Group, QWest, Blue Cross/Blue Shield and Farm Bureau. He works with small businesses, too.*

Steve serves as a Trustee for Kiwanis International, is a member of the Board of Governors for Iowa Easter Seals and has served as Chairman of the Board for Fellowship of Christian Athletes. The National Speakers Association has awarded Steve the Certified Speaking Professional (CSP), their highest earned designation.

Contact Information
Steve Siemens, CSP
Siemens People Builders
6478 N.E. 5th Avenue.
Des Moines, IA 50317-9102
Phone (888) SAY STEVE
Phone (515) 265-8748
Fax (515) 265-5750
Email steve@ThePeopleBuilder.com
Website: www.ThePeopleBuilder.com

CREATING BALANCE AT WORK

by Deborah Kern, Ph.D.

H ave you ever noticed that people have very different physical and mental reactions to stress? Some gain weight. Some lose weight. Some can't sleep. Some can't wake up. Some get anxious and fearful. Some get frustrated and irritable. As a nurse and health educator in the early 1980's and a hospital administrator in the early 1990's, I noticed it, too — and I was frustrated that our stress management programs had a "one-size-fits-all" approach to helping people deal with the stress in their lives.

Finally, in the process of doing mind/body research I discovered an ancient health science system from India that addressed individual approaches to stress management. The key is to learn what your nature is and then learn how to keep yourself in balance in order to prevent the harmful effects that stress can have on your health, your relationships, and your ability to enjoy your work. In this chapter you will not only learn what your mind/body type is, but you will also learn some practical ways to create balance even when feeling stressed at work.

One Size Does Not Fit All

We all have a unique nature: a unique body type, a unique personality, and unique strengths and weaknesses. You probably learned in your middle school health class that three body types exist: ectomorph — the thin, petite build; mesomorph — the medium, muscular build; and endomorph — the fleshy, stocky build. Although this information is widely accepted in the health science field, we rarely use it to customize health programs, and we never use it to help people manage stress!

You also have probably taken some form of personality typing test such as Myers Briggs or True Colors. This is another way to determine individual differences, but it does not address physical differences such as skin texture, body size, and energy levels. The Ayurveda approach I am going to share with you is like a combination of the body typing system (endomorph, ectomorph, mesomorph) and the personality typing systems. Using the Ayurveda approach is a great way to learn how to manage your unique physical and mental reactions to stress by staying "in balance."

Ayurveda: A Mind/Body Approach

Ayurveda is a 5,000-year-old health science from India. It literally means "The Science of Life." According to Ayurvedic principles, whenever a person is stressed (whether it is physical, emotional, or spiritual stress) they get "out of balance." Allowing ourselves to remain in a prolonged state of stress keeps the mind/body in a permanent state of imbalance. Eventually our systems collapse from exhaustion.

The Ayurvedic health system identifies the specific physical and psychological differences in individuals. Physical (thin, solid, dark, or pale), mental (quick-witted, thoughtful, or good memory), emotional (high strung, temperamental, or calm) and social characteristics (talkative, loyal, or generous) can be identified and then classified into three distinct mind/body types. In Sanskrit, the ancient language of India, the three mind/body types are called Vata, Pitta, and Kapha. But to make things easier to understand I have re-named them for this book as Air, Fire, and Earth.

The following questionnaire is designed to help you determine your mind/body type and how it is expressed in your physical, emotional, and mental self. You will immediately notice that the questionnaire is brief and highly subjective. That's because it is designed to help you learn more about yourself, not to label you. When answering the questions, place a check beside the answer that best describes your nature: in other words, the answer that best describes the general patterns of your life, not just how you have been feeling lately. If you absolutely can't make up your mind, you may check more than one or leave the item blank. When you have completed the questions, total the number of checks in each of the columns.

This questionnaire is not intended to precisely and accurately diagnose or label you. It is meant to give you an idea of your tendencies and areas of dominance. If you were to visit an Ayurvedic physician, you would fill out a much lengthier questionnaire and have a one-hour interview and pulse diagnosis with the physician to determine your mind/body type.

Mind/Body Type Questionnaire

Please check the response that best describes you:

1. Hair texture	__ dry, curly, full of body	__ straight, fine	__ thick, wavy, shiny
2. Hair color	__ medium or light brown	__ blond or reddish tone or early gray	__ dark brown, black
3. Skin Texture	__ on the dry side	__ delicate, sensitive	__ oily, smooth
4. Complexion (compared to others of same race)	__ darker	__ more reddish, freckled	__ lighter
5. Bone Size	__ small	__ average	__ large
6. Eyes	__ small	__ medium	__ large
7. Weight	__ thin, hard to gain	__ average	__ heavy, easy to gain
8. Run like a	__ deer	__ tiger	__ bear
9. Energy level	__ fluctuates, to come in waves	__ is moderate or high, can push myself too hard	__ is steady
10. Preferred climate	__ dislike cold; comfortable in warm and hot weather	__ dislike heat; perspire easily; thrive in winter	__ dislike damp cold, tolerate extremes well

11. Typical hunger level	__ can vary from excessive to no interest in food	__ is intense, need regular meals	__ is usually low but can be emotionally driven
12. Sleep pattern	__ interrupted, light	__ sound, moderate	__ deep, long; awaken slowly
13. Typical dreams	__ flying, looking down at the ground, jumping, chase scenes	__ fire, violence, anger	__ oceans, clouds, romance
14. Sexual interest	__ strong when romantically involved, low to moderate otherwise	__ moderate to strong	__ slow to awaken, but sustained; generally strong
15. Most sensitive to	__ noise	__ bright light	__ strong odors
16. Emotional moods	__ change easily, very responsive	__ quick tempered, intense	__ even tempered, slow to anger
17. Reaction to stress	__ anxious, fearful	__ irritated	__ mostly calm
18. Spending habits	__ am easy and impulsive	__ am careful, but I spend	__ tend to save, accumulate
19. Mental activity	__ quick mind, restless	__ sharp intellect, aggressive	__ calm, steady, stable
20. Preferred learning style	__ listening to a speaker	__ reading or using visual aids	__ associating it with another memory
21. Memory	__ short term best	__ good overall __ clear, precise; detailed	__ long term best
22. Manner of speaking	__ fast and often excessive		__ soothing, slow, with moments of silence
23. Most out standing trait	__ vivacious	__ determined	__ easy going
24. Friendships	__ easily adapt to different kinds of people	__ often choose friends on the basis of their values	__ am slow to make new friends but forever loyal

25. Friends and family say I should be more	__ settled	__ tolerant	__enthusiastic
Totals	__ AIR	__ FIRE	__ EARTH

All of us have some air, some fire, and some earth. But our "recipes" are different. For instance, my two most dominant characteristics are air and earth, and I have very little fire in my nature. The goal is not to have a balance of each of the characteristics (that would be the same mistake as making everyone be the same body type), but the goal is to keep each of the characteristics you express in its balanced state.

As you learn about the characteristics of each of the three mind/body types, you will find that some of them fit you very well and others don't. You may find that mentally you express one characteristic and physically you express another, or that your skin and hair express one while your digestion and energy level express another. This is perfectly normal. What's important is that you begin tuning into yourself and noticing how you feel when you are balanced and when you are "not quite yourself."

Air in Balance

Air is associated with lightness, quickness, and dryness. A person who has dominant Air is light, imaginative, joyous, sensitive, creative, quick-minded, exhilarated, and spontaneous. When a person with a dominant Air nature is in balance, she has an abundance of quick energy but may tire easily. She is often very funny and charming, and she tends to interrupt the conversation and then forgets what she wanted to say; however, you forgive her because you know it's completely unintentional.

Air Out of Balance

When under stress, the Air person's quick mind begins to move so quickly that it spins uncontrollably, preventing her from completing a thought — let alone a project. This makes her forgetful and keeps her awake at night, even though her body is exhausted. Then, as her mind continues to spin, she begins to feel worried, anxious, and fearful. She often forgets to eat — which makes her feel even more "light headed" and "spacey." In her physical body, she often experiences spasms, chills, shakiness, constipation, or gas.

Restoring Balance to Air

To stay in balance, it is very important for Air people to be regular in life (keeping a regular schedule for meals, sleeping, and other needed activities) and to compensate for a relative lack of stability in the body's functioning. Rest and warmth are also essential in keeping Air balanced. But probably the most significant practice for an Air person to maintain is the practice of calming the mind. That is why meditation and relaxation are vital parts of this person's healthy lifestyle.

Susan's Story: Anxiety, Insomnia and Weight Loss

One of my clients, Susan, was a typical Air type. When she filled out the questionnaire, all but three of the check marks fell into the Air category. She was a petite, vivacious, and outgoing person who worked in sales. All of her clients loved her. In fact, they wanted to work only with her when placing an order. As the business grew, Susan hired new staff to help with the growing demands. Unfortunately, her workload continued to increase because she felt compelled to serve the clients who demanded her involvement. She began to come in early and work through her lunch break, just to meet the increased workload. Her weight began to drop, and she was feeling very anxious. Her anxiety prevented her from sleeping at night, even though she was exhausted from her work.

When she first came to see me, Susan was taking tranquilizers and seeing a psychologist twice a week. She was overwhelmed with life. She said she felt like a hamster in a cage, endlessly running on a wheel and never getting anywhere. It was clear that the nature of her job was pushing her Air nature out of balance. Although the creativity and the contact with people was satisfying her, the relentless pace and the overcrowded, noisy office were driving her out of balance.

Keeping Air In Balance

To help her become more balanced so she could view her situation more clearly, I recommended that Susan take the following steps:
1. Eat several small, warm meals throughout the day.
2. Practice deep breathing at least 3 times a day.
3. Make things as quiet as possible in her car and her home.
4. Do not watch the news before going to bed.
5. Take a warm bath and drink Chamomile tea an hour before going to bed.
6. Turn out the lights by 10 p.m.
7. Do progressive muscle relaxation in bed before falling asleep.
8. Practice 20 minutes of meditation in the early morning.

After practicing these suggestions for two weeks, Susan felt much better. She was able to stop taking her medication, and she began to think clearly enough in her therapy sessions to make decisions about how to make changes in her life. Well-rested and clear-headed, she made the decision to change jobs. Within a month, she was back to her cheerful, enthusiastic self.

Fire in Balance

A Fire person in balance is often courageous, clearheaded, successful, enterprising, joyous, competitive, and sharp minded. He has a medium build with hair that is reddish, graying, or balding (the ancient wisdom says that, because the fire is so hot, it either turns the hair red, burns the color out or burns the hair off the top of the head!). A Fire-dominant person is intense and has a strong digestion. He is very articulate, decisive, efficient, and organized. He has a good sense of judgment and critical thinking skills.

Fire Out of Balance

When stressed, Fire often turns a sharp mind into a sharp tongue, good judgment into judgmentalism, and critical thinking into simply critical. The out-of-balance Fire person becomes easily frustrated and irritated and may become fanatical about organization and perfection. He may be so focused on achieving a goal that he overworks himself and allows no time for relaxation and rejuvenation.

Restoring Balance to Fire

To stay in balance, it is very important for Fire people to remain cool and eat timely meals. Remember, if the digestive fires have nothing to burn, they will burn the people you are with! Practicing non-judgment is a must for Fire out of balance. Since they have highly developed judgment skills, they often have a hard time turning judgment off. This causes them to go more and more out of balance. The most important thing for a person with Fire out of balance to do is to let go of the need to have things go the way they think they should go!

Ron's Story: Frustration, Perfectionism and a Sharp Tongue

Ron manages a staff of 36 people. His doctor had advised him that unless he made a change in the stress level of his job, his high blood pressure and peptic ulcers would force him to quit. He left a high-powered corporate management position to work for the state government. He hoped that the smaller staff and more regular work hours would help him manage his stress better. On the contrary, his stress level had risen!

When Ron arrived at his new position, he immediately saw ways to improve the system. He designed new inventory systems and developed a new case management system which would help save hours of meetings each week. Unfortunately, Ron's new ideas had to first be approved by several committees and then had to pass through a cumbersome bureaucracy before being implemented. The first month, Ron was annoyed, but he managed to contain his irritation. The second month, he was very frustrated and found himself speaking sharply to some of his employees. And by the third month, Ron was blowing up at the smallest incident.

For Ron, the solution was simple, but not easy. I recommended that he begin packing a lunch every day so he could eat when he was hungry.

This always helps a person with dominant Fire. The main cause of his imbalance was the anger he felt when his ideas and plans were not accepted and carried out immediately. This reaction is very common for people with dominant fire. Their sharp minds and good organizational skills help them develop excellent strategies, but when people don't follow their plan, they become very irritated. *They must let go of the need to have things go the way they think they should go.* This is not what Ron wanted to hear. But when he realized how much his need for the perfect plan was affecting his health, he was able to let go. When he did, his blood pressure dropped, his acid indigestion improved, and his wife noticed the difference in his personality, too!

Earth in Balance

A person who is dominant Earth is strong, steady, wise, serene, and earthy. She has strong bones, strong teeth, and the capability of storing energy — which may result in a well-proportioned, heavier body. She is often voluptuous with beautiful large eyes, and she is compassionate and calm. In her healthy state, Earth is forgiving, deliberate, and able to save money and keep friends. Earth people are often unflappable and very loyal.

Earth Out of Balance

When stressed, the slow, steady nature of Earth can become so slow it gets stuck. The body continues to store fluids or fat. Emotionally, the person clings to possessions and relationships that she needs to release. Instead of spinning out of control like Air or flaring out with a hot temper like Fire, Earth out of balance becomes lethargic and depressed.

Restoring Balance to Earth

To stay in balance, it is very important for Earth to keep moving. Physical movement is the best way to bring Earth back in balance. It also helps to stay warm and dry, seek variety in daily activities, and clean out the clutter in the office, home and car! The diet that helps balance Earth is one that reduces dairy products and sweet, heavy foods.

But the most important thing is to *keep moving!*

Karen's Story: Lethargy, Depression and Overeating

Karen owns a quaint restaurant that specializes in European cuisine. After her business partner had a stroke, she found herself managing the workload of two people while her partner recuperated. Luckily, Karen's dominant Earth nature provided her with the stamina to work long hours, as well as the compassion to help nurture her partner back to health. However, the emotional shock of her partner's sudden illness, combined with the anxiety of keeping the business alive, drove Karen to the refrigerator, freezer, or pantry late at night to soothe herself. After a couple of months of nightly food indulgences, Karen put on 20 pounds. Now, instead of getting out of bed to do her early morning walk, she was hitting the snooze on her alarm clock. She began to feel lethargic all day long. By the time she came to see me, she was very depressed about her weight gain. She felt hopeless.

Balancing Earth is pretty straightforward: Lighten up and get moving! The first thing I suggested for Karen was to find a way to move around more throughout the day. Her days were spent mostly sitting at a desk, talking on the phone or working at the computer, while her nights were spent greeting guests and overseeing restaurant operations. Of course her first reaction was to say that she just didn't have time to exercise until her partner was well — and she was right. She absolutely didn't have time to go to a gym, change clothes, take a class or walk on a treadmill, shower, and drive back to work. But she did have time to wake up 20 minutes earlier than she had been and ride her exercise bike before showering for the day. And she did have time to walk for 20 minutes during her lunch hour. Once she added this bit of activity into her days she immediately began feeling better. It was easier for her to resist eating heavy lunches knowing that she was getting ready for a walk, and the walk gave her just the boost she needed to make it past her normal 3 p.m. candy bar and soft drink. She lost some weight, but more importantly she felt energized and hopeful again.

How to use this information:

All of us have a combination of Air, Fire, and Earth in our nature. And all of us can go out of balance in any one of the three areas, but it's most likely that we will go out of balance in the area that is our dominant nature. Here are six questions to ask yourself to see if you are in or out of balance:

1. Do I eat when I'm hungry and stop when I'm full?
2. Do I have plenty of energy for my day?
3. Do I sleep well at night?
4. Are my relationships good?
5. Is my elimination good?
6. Am I generally peaceful and joyous?

These are the six questions I ask myself, and I have my clients ask themselves, to determine if they are in or out of balance. If you answer no to any one of the questions, then ask yourself if it feels like Air, Fire, or Earth that is out of balance. Then take the appropriate steps to bring that element back into balance. Many times you will feel that one element is out of balance, and when you take steps to bring it back into balance, you suddenly feel that another one is out of balance. Just keep taking the necessary steps to bring each of them into balance. Creating balance is an ongoing process.

ABOUT
DEBORAH KERN, PH.D.

*W*hile some people talk about the body-mind connection, Dr. Deborah Kern helps people experience the link between the physical self and the emotional self. It's a path she's explored personally and professionally over the past twenty years. Coming from a traditional health promotion background, to awakening both personally and professionally to holistic ways of thinking and exploring healing, she is an ardent proponent of body wisdom. Deborah shares the power of it with other health professionals and the public.

Deborah is a forty-something wife and mother with a toddler and a teen, who combines family responsibilities with a demanding career, just like the people she counsels. She holds a doctorate in Health Studies from Texas Woman's University and an M.B.A. from the University of Texas. Her mission is to help people "feel" the science of the body-mind connection. Through their active participation in her motivating keynote presentations, people discover the patterns in their lives and are inspired to make positive lifestyle changes necessary to enhance not only their physical health, but their work, their relations and their spiritual well being.

Contact Information:
Deborah Kern, Ph.D.
605 County Road 1184
Cullman, AL 35057
Phone: (256) 775-3716
Fax: (413) 751-5109
E-mail:Dr.Deb@DeborahKern.com
Website: www.DeborahKern.com

BUILD UP YOUR ABILITY TO BOUNCE BACK FROM SETBACK

by Caterina Rando, M.A., M.C.C

W hen you think about what it takes to be successful in your career over the long haul, you might cite a need for intelligence, determination, strategic thinking, or the ability to communicate ideas effectively. When you think about what it takes to be successful in your personal life, you might cite the ability to be a good friend, to be a good partner, and to live with passion. While all these and other character traits will facilitate one's ability to create good results in life, there is another important characteristic that often goes unrecognized and is rarely discussed. That important character trait is resilience: your ability to successfully bounce back from setback. Our resilience is built up only by actually being resilient when need be. When you successfully drive to your destination after a near-miss accident, you are being resilient. When you continue with your work day and are able to be productive after a difficult confrontation with a co-worker, you are being resilient. When you lose a loved one, or a job, or your life savings and choose to continue to get out of bed each morning and go on, you are being resilient.

Put attention on increasing your resilience, and you will find yourself experiencing more joy and fulfillment in your personal and professional life. In coaching and training entrepreneurs, executives, and people in job transition, I've noticed that how people react to what is done to them is more significant in their long-term success than the setbacks they may or may not encounter. We can make detailed strategic plans, begin daily activities to move us forward, put structures in place that support us in creating what we want — still the world will always throw us unexpected changes and unanticipated events. Betty Talmadge, meat broker and cookbook author, is the one who first said, "Life is what happens to you when you're making other plans." We cannot control anything or anyone else, and we create a lot of disappointment and frustration (as well as waste a lot of our life energy) when we try. You have no control over setbacks, but you can control how you react to them.

Life happens. You might be passed over for a promotion. The bid you've worked on for three weeks might go to another firm; your great assistant could move to Tahiti. Your computer and its contents could be consumed by a virus; your building could be flooded or your car stolen. At some point in everyone's life, setback occurs.

How you respond to what happens is what will make the greatest difference for you. Your resilience is what gives you the ability to get back up after you have been knocked down — even after the second and third rounds of having your plans pummeled. Choose right now to become more resilient. Regardless of how much experience and success you already have at bouncing back, there is always room for improvement.

Let's put your bounce-back ability through a strength-training program. Follow these principles to soar through setbacks and keep your resilience revved up so that when you need it, it will be right there for you, and you will be ready to step forward and get into action.

Let It Out

Talk it out with an advisor, write it out in your journal, cry it out on your couch, sweat it out in the gym. Do whatever it takes to purge yourself of the emotion you feel over this setback. The bigger the setback, the longer it takes — and the more emotion you have to purge. Do not stifle feelings about the setback; acknowledge your anger, sadness, frustration, or fear. Once you're in touch with those feelings, work on releasing them. A sense of closure or completion, which eventually leads to peace, is necessary in order to move forward.

Let it Go

Eighty percent of what we think about has already happened. What a waste. Don't waste your time and precious energy thinking about what went wrong yesterday, what you forgot to include in your letter, why you did not get the sale. Do a quick review and then let it go. Dwelling on yesterday depletes your stamina to be successful today and tomorrow. If you keep looking in the rear view mirror you are going to get yourself into a crash. Ann Richards, the former governor of Texas, said "always look forward; never look back." Maybe you have to forgive yourself or others for past mistakes, maybe you have to make amends for a past error in judgment. If so, do it. Do not dwell on it. Some people have a natural tendency to dwell and think about things for weeks and months before taking action. If you are like that, begin to train and coach yourself to take action and achieve resolution faster. Otherwise your life cannot move forward because it is stuck in the past. Let it go, or clean it up and then let it go and move on. Do it now.

Look for the Lesson

Setbacks serve. They bring with them lessons about you, about life, about relationships. When a setback erupts in your path, do not dowse the flames without first examining its lesson. Learning the lessons that your setbacks deliver to you is one of the ways you build your resilience. Prepare yourself for the next surprise by learning something from this one — look for the lesson.

Ask Yourself a Powerful Question

To assist you in finding the lesson, reflect on the situation, journal on it, and ask the right questions. Instead of asking yourself questions that further burden you — like "How could this happen to me?" or "What did I do to deserve this?" — ask yourself powerful questions that help build your resilience. Find ways to uplift yourself; shift your view of the situation by asking questions such as "How can I turn things around?" and "How can I support myself during this challenging time?"

Even if you don't get an answer right away, keep asking yourself these powerful questions until the guidance that will best serve you appears.

Be Your Own Resilience Coach

You can hire a business or personal coach, you can visit a therapist, and you can gain support from a friend over coffee any afternoon. None of these valuable support structures can make as much of a difference as you deciding that it is your responsibility and choice to support yourself to do what is in your best interest and to do what will build up your resilience. You are the only one who is with you twenty-four hours a day — seven days a week. What do you tell yourself when you are with yourself? Do you tell yourself that this setback is temporary; do you tell yourself that you are better off without that promotion because the next opportunity will be even better? Or, do you tell yourself you are a failure; you are no good, unworthy? Begin to pay attention to what you tell yourself about yourself because you are listening. You have this chatter in your head all the time. For some reason when there is a setback, you begin to listen to yourself more, and if you are not saying supportive things to yourself, that will not serve you. I have a rule I want you to adopt — No negative self-talk.

Do not allow yourself to put yourself down and speak negatively about yourself. Be on your side, not on your back. Pick yourself up with your self-talk. Do not knock yourself down.

Mourn the Death of What Will Not Be

Sometimes people cannot find a way back up after they have fallen down because a long held dream or goal has died. Think of the college athlete who is on his way to being a professional athlete when he suffers an injury that prevents him from ever playing again: a dream of being a professional athlete died. Maybe you have been part of a loving couple whose relationship became strained beyond repair; with that breakup a dream of a happily-ever-after relationship with that person died. Or perhaps you were being groomed for a promotion when your company merges with another, and instead of a promotion you get a pinkslip. With that event a dream of you in your new role died, too. A dream is a vision, a picture we hold in our mind of what we are working to create in our lives. When we become aware that what we have been pursuing — what we have been passionate about, what we have planned for and prepared for with time, energy and resources — is no longer possible for us, it is time to mourn. Usually the mourning will come without effort; the tears, the exhaustion, even depression will enter with the awareness that what we coveted is outside our control and will not come to us. We can feel unwilling to go forward. "Why bother?" is a question we might ask ourselves.

Recognize that mourning is the first step to bouncing back from any setback. Mourning is not only important when a person we loved has passed on. Mourning will serve us when a dream dies, a special situation ends, or any kind of loss occurs. Give yourself time to mourn. Cry, journal, sleep late, walk on the beach, wear your pajamas all day until you get sick of mourning. At that point the bounce-back begins to start.

Redefine Your Vision

When the mourning slows down, it is time for a new vision. If your vision was to be top salesperson of the year and you did not make it, the new vision might be to get it the next year or the vision might be completely different. The new vision might be to switch to a better company, start your own company or leave sales and start to teach high school again. It is OK to have your new vision be to begin searching for a vision or spend time rejuvenating yourself or reconnect with the true happiness you lost somewhere along the way. A vision is an intention that sets the direction. You may not be sure which road is the shortest, safest, or smoothest, but by selecting a vision you tell your feet which way to turn.

When you have a clear vision of what you want, every morning take two minutes to do a brief visualization of having achieved your desired outcome. See a vivid mental picture of that large commission check in hand, of you signing the contract or overseeing the installation of the equipment you are selling, or selecting your wedding dress, or sitting on the stairs of your first home. Whatever success is to you, see it. Hold that picture in your mind throughout the day. Reconnect with that picture in your mind throughout the day to add momentum and energy to your actions. Hold on to your new vision.

Build on Past Successes

Sometimes your setback might seem too much to handle. There may be times you find it hard to go on, especially after the significant personal loss of a relationship or a loved one. To help yourself bounce back during such difficult times, think about other challenges that you have faced in your lifetime. Remember that you lived through getting dumped the day before your prom, getting fired from your first good job, breaking your leg. Your life went on and you came out better off. Think about how you dealt with those situations — and how you came through them. What worked for you at those times? Was it taking a vacation, talking to a counselor, watching "I Love Lucy" reruns, or taking a leave of absence from your job? Whatever it was, ask yourself if it is time to do it again.

Thinking and Planning Time

When we experience a moderate or major setback, we are at risk of having the next setback (no matter how small) be the one that will break our will to keep going. That is why, when a setback occurs, you need to make sure that you have lots of reasons to get up each morning. Setting aside daily thinking and planning time is always good. In times of setback be extra diligent about making sure at the end of each day you take time to plan for the next day. During that time identify what you want to accomplish tomorrow, what resources you need to do that, what questions you need answered. Planning allows you to be proactive rather than reactive, thereby feeling more control after a time when you have just felt out of control.

Use Your Power of Choice

Build up your resilience with choosing to respond well to life's everyday small setbacks. Do not let traffic, a rude comment, a delayed plane, a spilled cup of coffee, or a disappointing phone call ruin your whole day. Consciously choose to bounce right back. Remember, we do not always have a choice in what happens to us — but we always have a choice about how we react to it. Every day as you begin your day set an intention that you are going to have a good day, and that any small setbacks you might encounter will not set you off course. Again, reconnect to your vision.

Get Some New Support

One mistake people often make after a setback is they try to do everything because keeping busy gives them a sense of control. This will ensure that a setback is replaced by burnout rather than resilience. What are the activities you can delegate or farm out? Is it time to hire a cleaning person, a gardener, a dog walker two days a week? Is it time to get your groceries, dry cleaning, or dinners delivered? Pick one new support structure to bring in. Your time is best spent on those things that only you can do. When you feel supported in your work, you will have more stamina.

Stay Centered

You have to remember that situations are not constant. If you lose your job, you will not always be without a job. If your car is smashed, that does not mean you will never have another car. If your sweetheart leaves you, that does not mean no one will ever love you again.

When your book proposal is rejected again, that does not mean you cannot write. When you burn the lasagna, that does not mean you cannot cook. When you pick your child up late from daycare, that does not mean you are a bad parent. One setback, any setback, we experience does not define us when we hold our center. Holding your center means that you develop the ability to be calm, rational, and objective in the face of setback, difficulty, and adversity. You remember that you are powerful. You call on your inner resources, and you apply the principles of resilience.

Get a New Perspective

What are some things you want to do that you have been putting off? Whenever I go visit my friend who lives in Europe I come home with a different perspective. I am reminded that life needs to include more fun. A new perspective can be found in your own town. Go to seminars, talk to new colleagues, and get a coach or a mentor. Pursue other opportunities that will improve the personal side of your life. A focus on freshness will soothe your soul and feed your spirit and stamina.

What have you been putting off? Maybe it is time to start yoga, go back to school, or join a community volunteer group. Having new experiences and perhaps finding some new passions, in the process of gaining a new perspective, will get your creative juices going, rebuild any lost confidence, and cause you to enjoy your life more. Also you never know where these new things can take you.

Schedule Rejuvenation

Sometimes when we experience a setback, it can kick us into high gear. We force ourselves to try harder, work longer, do more. If setbacks motivate you to take action, that's fine — as long as it is not at the expense of your self-nurturing. Self-nurturing, the time spent rejuvenating your energy and replenishing your spirit, is more important after a setback than at any other time. Go get a massage, take a yoga class, melt in a tub of lavender suds, or chat endlessly on the phone with a friend. Do whatever it is that deeply nourishes you. Make the care and feeding of you a top priority during times of personal challenge. It will ensure that you bounce back faster.

Play, Play, Play

The great 20th century actress and philosopher, Mae West, said, "Too much of a good thing can be wonderful." We often forget that the pursuit of pleasure is a good thing. I am guessing you might be like a lot of busy, motivated people with a vision. You are focused; you do not want to waste time, and if you have any free time you fill it with work. Not because you necessarily enjoy working more than anything else in your life but because it is the easiest, most convenient way for you to get results, build esteem, and feel yourself experiencing satisfaction.

If you have not played for awhile — play can be challenging, it can be uncomfortable. You ask yourself, what will I do, where will I go, what will I wear? You forget how to play because you do not do it much unless it is to benefit your children. Go ahead right now and make a list of 25 things that you consider play. Not rejuvenating things like a sauna, massage or jog, but play activities that you would enjoy like drawing or singing or feeding the ducks stale bread. Do not keep reading until you have your list of twenty-five things. Go ahead — I'll wait.

Now take that list and schedule some play time this week. Spend at least twenty minutes doing something for the pure fun of it. Maybe you go rollerblading, or bake a chocolate cake, or sit and watch your favorite classic TV reruns.

The following week take two play times and the next week three until you are taking some play time most days. Every time you complete something on the list, add something else.

Most of us used to know how to play although somewhere along the way we forgot how. During your playtime you will be rejuvenating on an emotional level, and you will be using parts of your brain you do not usually use. Ideas will begin to flow and more serenity will be restored in your life. You will begin to get better at playing. Playing will become easier for you and you will not resist it any more.

Practice Patience

If you receive a setback in the form of a car accident, or a debilitating illness, it is in your best interest to practice being patient with yourself. Susan, who had always been fit and energetic, was in a near-fatal car accident. She was left with a neck brace, chronic pain, and her ability to move at all was significantly compromised. Susan went to yoga class twice a day for two years to get herself back to being as vital as before the accident. She was patient with herself in the beginning when she could barely raise her leg, and she was patient with herself as time went on if she felt she was not healing fast enough.

In racquetball a bounce of the ball back from the wall is immediate. In life a bounce back can take a long time, even years. Susan worked hard to relieve her body of pain and gain her flexibility back. Being patient does not mean waiting for a situation to heal itself only through the passage of time. Being patient includes being proactive and in action. The distinction here is to trust that you will bounce back through giving yourself what you need while loving yourself in the process.

It is your ability to bounce back after setbacks that will keep you successful and fulfilled over the long haul of your career and your life. What matters is not how many times you find yourself face down in the sand, but how many times you get back up and dust yourself off. Take just one of these principles to start with, then add another and another until resilient responses are second nature to you. As you build these skills, why not start the day with this bold affirmation: "Go ahead, Life, send me a setback. I eat setbacks for breakfast; they are great fuel for the day!"

ABOUT
CATERINA RANDO, M.A., M.C.C.

*C*aterina Rando, M.A., M.C.C., is a speaker with solutions. She is an international speaker, business success coach and writer. Caterina is known for her interactive, high-energy and high-content programs. She is the author of* Power Thinking *and is featured as a success expert in three leading business books:* Get Clients Now!, The 11 Commandments of Wildly Successful Women, *and the* NAFE Guide to Starting Your Own Business. *She shows attendees how to take the steps to cultivate the skills they need to reach more personal and professional success. As an award-winning professional speaker, trainer and facilitator, Caterina has designed and delivered a variety of customized programs for businesses, educational organizations and associations in the United States and abroad. Her clients include Hewlett Packard, Lucent, Restoration Hardware, Oral B, and Lightwave Electronics.*

Caterina is a member of the National Speakers Association, the Board of Directors of the San Francisco Chamber of Commerce and Herald Business College's Advisory Committee. She is a columnist for several internet sites and has made several media appearances, including NBC News, *Moscow television and Romanian radio programs.*

Contact Information:
Caterina Rando
182 22nd Avenue
San Francisco, CA 94121
Phone: (415) 668-4535
Phone: (800) 966-3603
Fax: (415) 668-6450
E-mail: CPR@CaterinaR.com
Website: www.CaterinaR.com

CHANGE YOUR THINKING, CHANGE YOUR LIFE

by Suzie Dawson

This book covers many different viewpoints on how to reduce stress. Delegating tasks, simplifying your life, meditation, and exercise are among the methods commonly mentioned here and in other sources. The one key ingredient that seems to often be missing is that stress is a result of our thoughts. As a famous proverb goes, "As he (man) thinketh in his heart, so is he." You can try all the external ways to reduce stress you want, but without an internal shift in thinking, there is little hope of maintaining a lower stress level. Of that, you can be sure.

The idea that our thoughts create our reality has been around since the beginning of time. It has been written and spoken about for years, from biblical times to present day. So how does this relate to stress? The same way it relates to everything else in life. Your thoughts create your reality. If you focus on stress, you will get more stress. If you focus on peace, that is what you will get. You must change your thinking in order to create less stress in your life.

This idea may seem too simplistic for many. "How can this be?" you ask. "It has to be more complicated than that! If this is all there is to it, why isn't everybody changing their thinking?" These are all great questions to which I do not have all the answers. What I can share with you is a different approach to creating a new, more peaceful reality.

The one common denominator in all stressed people is the idea that what is causing their stress is bigger than they are. The paper work on their desk is bigger, the endless chores are bigger, the incoming bills are bigger, and all the appointments they have are bigger. It is very easy to get overwhelmed by everything. Recognizing that *you* are bigger and more powerful than *all of it* is the way out!

This leads to the first step to less stress, which is to recognize yourself as the creator of your circumstances. Take responsibility for everything. This will empower you. Realize that you have created the stress in your life by your thinking and the choices you have made. If you are serious about reducing the stress in your life, this part is critical.

Many people fail to embrace this step. The belief is that they are the victims of their circumstances. This belief makes it very difficult to change anything. It is much more empowering to realize that you are the one responsible for where you are. It is very easy to fall into the "life is happening and I'm just along for the ride" or the "poor me" attitudes. If this applies to you, it is time to *stop* and let it go.

This may require diligence on your part, for it is easy to succumb to the "victim mentality." It is equally as easy to take responsibility for your life. It is not more difficult, just a result of making different choices. You may have "chosen" to let life happen to you, and now you choose not to. It is as simple as that. You may want to try an affirmation to help with this step, such as "I embrace my power" or "I am the creator of my circumstances." Whatever works for you. The point is to create a defining statement that will help you to feel powerful in your life. An important part to this step is to feel powerful as you say it. It is not enough just to blurt out the words. You must feel it as you speak it. You may want to try posting little notes around your home or office or carrying a note card with your empowering statement on it. This routine will help to reinforce this idea for you.

One of my clients, Mary, has been working to create a more peaceful existence. Her life is extremely hectic. From the moment she wakes up in the morning, she is in high gear. She starts the day by making breakfast and getting her two little girls ready for school, then it is on to household chores, then bills, then lunch, then dinner, and on and on and on. Sound familiar? Your job may be different; however, I am sure you can relate to that same feeling that "it is all never ending" or that "there is too much to do in too little time."

The first area we went to work on was helping Mary to feel more powerful in her life. Before any other changes could be made, this had to be addressed. I asked her to come up with a defining statement that made her feel strong and meditate on it for a few minutes each day. I also suggested that she repeat this statement every time she felt like things were "getting out of hand." I knew that it was important for her to start feeling strong before moving on to the other steps.

I then asked her to name three ways she could feel more powerful in her life. I knew she had the answers within her; I just needed to ask the right questions. She was able to easily come up with three. The first was to get the family on the same eating schedule. She had been making meals several times throughout the day to accommodate different family members. This was making her feel extremely scattered. The second way was to start the day by taking time to get centered. She decided to dedicate 30 minutes each morning to writing in her journal and for quiet contemplation. This helped her to begin each day in a peaceful way, instead of getting immediately out of bed and feeling as if she was "off to the races." The third way she came up with was to stop working at a certain time each day. As a housewife, working at home, she tended to keep going until late at night completing household chores. I suggested that people who work 9-to-5 jobs get to leave their work behind at a certain time, and so should she. This helped her to create more balance in her life, which immediately led to less stress.

We all have the answers within us if we will just take the time to ask. If it feels like this is just more "stuff" you have to do, start small and work your way up. Ask yourself, "What one thing can I do today that will give me a sense of control in my life?" This will help clarify which area to work on first. The point of all this is to recognize that this is your life, and you get to choose how to live it!

The second step to creating less stress is to change your thinking. As I stated earlier, your thoughts create your reality. What you focus on expands. If your focus is on stress, that is what you will get more of. I know this seems a difficult concept when you are constantly barraged with stressful situations. The answer lies in focusing on the positive and not the negative. If you think, "I have too much to do," you will immediately feel overwhelmed. If your thought is, "I am fully capable of handling all that I have to do," you will feel competent to take care of everything. One way to change your thinking is to begin asking, "How can I create more peace and harmony in my life?" This simple question can quickly change your circumstances because it immediately takes the focus off stress and on to how you can create peace. On one episode of a popular television comedy, the phrase "Serenity Now" was repeated throughout the show. Not a bad little phrase!

The key to this step is again, to not only think differently, but also to *feel* differently. There are numerous ways to do this. What I have found to be the quickest and most effective way is to think of the gifts in your life and feel gratitude for them. No matter how bad life may appear at any given moment, there are always things we can find for which to be thankful. Be thankful for your health, your family, or your home. If these don't apply, go outside and be thankful for nature. There is so much beauty around, if we will only let it in!

When I recently spoke with a new client, June, she was encountering many difficulties in her life. In our first conversation she listed several different things that were causing her distress. I told her that she must immediately get her focus off the sources of stress, and instead, begin feeling grateful for the gifts in her life. Her first question was, "How do I do this?" To which I answered, "Start making a list every morning of the things you are grateful for." This way, you will start out your day by feeling blessed, instead of focusing on and creating more problems.

Among the challenges people encounter when trying to change their thinking is that their attention is stuck on the negative. This situation is easily remedied. The solution is to take your attention off the cause of stress and place it onto something that makes you feel calm. This allows you to focus on peace and not stress, which in turn will help you to create more peace in your life. Here are some simple techniques to help change your focus.

1. Take a 5-minute breathing break.

Stop whatever you are doing, find a comfortable position, and focus on your breathing. Make sure your eyes are closed, and place all of your attention on your breath for the entire time. Be aware of how the breath feels going in and out of your body. When thoughts arise, simply notice them and return back to the breathing. This will help take your attention out of your head and off your stress.

2. Connect with your feelings.

The next time you find yourself stressed out, stop and ask if there is some inner feeling you do not want to experience. Try being still for a moment, take a few deep breaths, and let whatever feelings you have rise to the surface. Allow yourself to really let go and feel. We often keep ourselves busy and stressed out to avoid feeling. Being aware of our feelings makes us more available to the experiences life has to offer.

3. Get in touch with your senses.

Take a few minutes to look around your environment and notice what you see, hear, smell, taste and feel. Take each sense separately and give it your full attention for a minute or two. Get really curious about your surroundings. Notice the details of your environment. This will quickly bring your attention back into your body. So much time is often spent thinking, at the expense of all our senses.

4. Take a 10-minute play break.

Use this time to completely let go and have fun. Turn up some music and dance around, tell some jokes, or just "goof off." Do something fun that makes you feel good! Don't leave out this vital part of life! Feeling good is the best way to change your thinking. It is difficult, at best, to think positive thoughts when you are feeling bad.

5. Stop everything and do nothing.

This is not about taking time to read, talk with a friend, or meditate. This is about spending time with yourself and not doing anything. Resist the temptation to keep busy. Think of this as critical to your well-being! Remember that real growth comes when we are silent and available to receive messages, not when we are caught up playing the busy game of life.

These are all excellent ways to shift your attention, which is vital to changing your thinking. Think of taking these mini-breaks as essential to creating less stress. You must allow yourself a quick change of pace every now and then. We are not meant to be machines that are "on" all the time. Give yourself a break once in a while. You will be amazed at how refreshed you feel!

The last step is to surrender. Let it go. This step cannot be overlooked. Once you have assumed responsibility for your life and adjusted your thinking, you must let go. When you begin recognizing how easy it is to change your reality by changing your thoughts, it is easy to keep thinking positive thoughts so that you can create positive experiences. Keep in mind that if you are constantly thinking, you will not be present. There is a time when you must release the thoughts. Life is meant for feeling and experiencing, not for obsessive thinking!

The most important piece to this step is trust. Without trust, there will be no surrender. People often ask, "Why can't I let this go?" To which I reply, "Because you are not trusting that everything will work out in your favor." If you had full trust, it would be easy to let it go. So how do you begin trusting? Simply by making the decision to trust. Recognize that *not* trusting is fear-based. Do you prefer to come from a place of love or fear?

This brings to mind something that happened a few years ago. My husband had a life-long dream of owning a guitar. I decided to surprise him at Christmas with a gift certificate to a music store to buy the guitar of his choice. He was able to put down a couple hundred dollars on the chosen instrument, but fell short of the total price needed and was determined not to use a credit card. He got so anxious about getting the guitar that he could barely stand it. It was all he thought about for days. The good news was that his thoughts and excitement for it were naturally attracting the guitar to him. The bad news was that he started obsessing over it, in an "I have to have it now" kind of way. One Friday, after getting particularly wound up over getting his guitar, he decided to let it go. He realized that he had been without it all of his life and a few more weeks would not matter. The very next day, we received a check from out of the blue for an amount that covered the additional cost of the guitar. The moment he surrendered, the guitar was his.

There is a message here for all of us. We can and should change our thinking to attract what we most want, but there is also a point when we must let it go and trust that the universe will provide. If you think about it, what good does constant worrying do anyway? Absolutely none. It will not help us to improve our circumstances. If anything, it will repel what we are trying to create because it shows a lack of trust. And trust is a vital part of the process of surrender. When we hold on tightly to something, there is no room for it to come into our lives.

The "power of positive thinking" is not a new idea. It has been around for many years, thanks to Dr. Norman Vincent Peale and countless others. I always felt that there must be more to it than that. It was a nice concept, but there had to be some deeper meaning involved. Come to find out, years later, that this is it: What we think about, we attract.

Remember that overcoming stress is a constant training of the mind. Every time you find yourself feeling stressed, simply shift your thoughts by using one of the exercises from this chapter or by thinking about something you feel grateful for. This way you will begin attracting positive experiences instead of negative experiences. Change your thinking, change your life. It is that simple.

How much easier could life be if we were to grasp this concept? Think of all of the struggle that could have been avoided. When you start to understand the impact of your thoughts, life will become much easier. After years of searching for an easier way, I finally got it. We are the product of our thoughts. Nothing more, nothing less.

Keep in mind that words do not teach, experience does. I challenge you to not only keep these ideas in mind, but to apply them in your life. Only by testing these principles for yourself, will you come to understand their impact. Keep an open mind, and trust that you are deserving of a more peaceful, stress-free life. It is just around the corner.

ABOUT
SUZIE DAWSON

*S*uzie Dawson is a life coach, speaker and author dedicated to helping individuals live their best life. She is a graduate of Coach University and a member of the International Coach Federation. Suzie combines years of study in personal development with several different healing modalities to help her clients create the life they most desire. Using intuition as her guide, her clients have amazing results.

Suzie's own quest for answers began after a particularly challenging youth. During this time, she decided to make a top priority of helping others to live life to the fullest. Now, as the founder of Chrysalis Coaching, she continues to encourage others to be the fullest expression of themselves. She achieves this through her speaking, writing and coaching. Her personal philosophy is, "Our outside world is a reflection of our inside. If you want to change your business or your life, start by looking inward." Suzie is the author of the Food for Thought *bi-monthly e-newsletter, which promotes healing, change and prosperity within the restaurant industry. For a complimentary issue, please contact Suzie.*

Contact Information:
Suzie Dawson
Chrysalis Coaching
12315 Jones Maltsberger #406
San Antonio, TX 78247
Phone: (210) 402-5424
E-mail: SuzieDawson@earthlink.net
Website: www.Chrysalis-Coaching.com

IT'S YOUR TIME TO BE WELL– STRESS MANAGEMENT AS PREVENTIVE MEDICINE

by Jane Sullivan-Durand, M.D.

If a close friend sincerely asked, "How are you doing?," what would you say? "Great! Never better!" Or would you say, "Truthfully, I feel lousy. I'm over-extended at work and home, and everywhere I turn I'm getting hassled. I live on caffeine because I'm tired all the time and can't seem to get enough rest. My head and back ache constantly, and now my family is complaining because I'm irritable. With a life like mine, who wouldn't be irritable? I wish I could do something about this, but I don't know what to do!"

Sound familiar? Up to forty percent of people have health problems due to stress, and most continue to suffer without much relief. This chapter is devoted to those of you who know that stress is affecting your health and want to do something about it. It is also for you who feel well now, but worry that if life continues in the same direction you may become ill.

You are wise to be concerned. Stress causes many symptoms, such as headaches, sleep problems, indigestion, bowel problems and sexual difficulties. It is also linked to more serious health problems, such as high blood pressure, anxiety, depression, chronic pain, and autoimmune diseases, such as thyroid problems and rheumatoid arthritis. In some people, stress can be downright deadly as it promotes heart disease and causes heart attacks. Stress is serious business when it comes to your health.

Speaking as an Expert . . .

When I told my hairdresser that I'd be writing a chapter in a book about stress, she laughed. Not a snicker, not a chuckle, but a full belly laugh! "Well that fits," she said. "You're an *expert* on that!" Frankly, I laughed too because she wasn't referring to my medical skills or knowledge of stress management.

She was referring to my *life*.

This woman has seen me every six weeks or so for the past twelve years. She has seen me rush in late or early because I wasn't sure of the appointment time and answer an emergency page with my hair dripping shampoo and balancing a baby on my hip. *She knows* that *I know* about stress because she knows my life. It's a real life, with the typical struggles and challenges of our times.

As a doctor, I also know that my "typical life" is a set-up for stress-related health problems. Indeed, I've had my share of stress symptoms–neck spasms, jaw pain, headaches — just to name a few. Yet being a doctor gave me great experience for figuring out how to treat these symptoms. By combining professional and personal knowledge, I developed a treatment protocol that worked for me and works for my patients. In this chapter, I will share the first steps of this protocol so that you can

- Learn the difference between "good stress" and distress
- Clarify which of your own symptoms are stress-related
- Begin to implement simple strategies to reverse the effect of stress on your health.

If you are under stress and still feel well, these steps can help you to recognize stress symptoms before health problems develop. In this way, stress management becomes the ultimate preventive medicine.

Is Stress Really Bad for You?

It's reasonable to question whether stress can cause illness. We all know people who actually thrive from stress. They feel most productive, most creative and get more accomplished when they are under stress.

And they aren't sick. Besides, isn't stress just a part of being alive? Life is hard sometimes; it does not always go the way we wanted or expected. So what exactly is the problem with stress?

Technically speaking, stress is not always a problem. Some stress can actually be good for you. When you are busy and doing a lot of things that you enjoy, the stress can be stimulating. It can motivate you, energize you, and give you a reason for being. But we all know that you can have too much of a good thing, and "busy-ness" is no exception. Over time, as you push to do more and more each day, the "wear and tear" on your body catches up with you. That is the problem.

Look at the graph below. Named the Yerkes-Dodson curve, it was originally developed to depict performance as stress increases. It also applies to your health.

Graph from A Clinical Guide to the Human Stress Response *by George Everly, 1989, Kluwer Plenum Publishing. Used with permission.*

When responsibilities are rising, stress can actually be good for you. It improves your performance, vitality and well-being. But only to a point. After stress levels rise for a while, you reach your peak and then begin the downhill slide. Any system can take only so much pressure before it begins to fail. The human body is no exception.

So stress is not the problem . . . but distress can be. Distress occurs when you have too many tasks or responsibilities to keep up with, even if you enjoy them. Of course, it's also what happens when you become bombarded with the negative stuff. Like serious illness in your family or friends. Or when the people in your organization or family all get together and decide that *you* are the problem. Or when you have a boss, spouse, children or friends that seem to need more than you can give. Or when you are trying to cope with physical pain, emotional pain, fatigue or some other symptom that keeps you from doing what you want to do.

Any situation which leads you to feel overwhelmed, frustrated, frightened, or intimidated can push you over into distress very quickly.

How Does Distress Make You Sick?

Your body hears "danger" when your mind perceives "distress." This message is communicated through a system of nerves (called the sympathetic nervous system) that runs from your brain and travels throughout your entire body. When these nerves are activated, your body shifts into a state of readiness to protect yourself from this "danger." Named the "fight or flight response," it involves a variety of changes that occur simultaneously.

- Muscle tone increases, making you stronger and more agile.
- Heart rate and blood pressure increase to keep up with the extra oxygen demand from the muscles.
- Stress hormones are released from various glands, which increase blood sugar and energy production.
- Skin becomes sweaty, releasing heat and increasing the palms' ability to grip.
- Digestion, intestinal activity and sexual function decrease, thus allowing the body to put all of its energy into self-protection.
- Behaviorally, we assume a posture of anxiety, irritability or defensiveness, thereby maintaining a readiness to attack others or to flee for safety.

So your body is prepared to defend you physically, even if the danger is not a physical threat. It also doesn't matter whether you truly are in danger. Any situation which leads you to be distressed — frightened, angry, worried, frustrated — will trigger these changes in your body. You will be prepared for the battle or the disaster, whether or not it comes.

This reaction is a primitive mechanism that has persisted since the days when our survival was dependent on our ability to defend our-selves. It certainly does come in handy when we are in physical danger, as people who have survived disasters can attest to. But these days when we hear bad news, are stuck in traffic, or have an argument with our partner, we can't resolve the situation by running fast or jumping high. So we find ourselves sitting or pacing while our heart pounds, our blood pressure rises and our muscle tension increases. We remain ready to defend or attack. At this point, most people either release their aggres-sion (road-rage, anyone?) or stuff the frustration inside. Neither of these reactions is healthy, as they only prolong the fight or flight response.

The good news is that while our body is dealing with all of this, another part of our nervous system is preparing to move into action. There is a second set of nerves (called the parasympathetic nervous system) that can reverse the changes of the fight or flight response. After the stress has eased and we begin to settle down, these nerves become activated. Your heart rate and blood pressure come down, muscle tension eases, stress hormone production decreases, digestion and intes-tinal activity resume. Your body is calmer, less agitated and ready to move on.

If you experienced only mild stressors a few times each day and resolved each one completely, you wouldn't develop stress-related ill-nesses because the parasympathetic nerves would keep your body healthy. That's often why people feel so much better after a relaxing vacation! But for most people, life is not a vacation. The stressors keep coming at a fast and furious pace and often aren't resolved before the next ones come around. Thus, the body stays in a state of agitation, and this is when stress-related disorders develop.

Here are some examples of what stress can do:

• *Muscle tension* — When muscle tone increases repeatedly, certain muscles can remain tight and painful, especially those that have been injured at some point. Some muscles can actually shift into spasm. This is how stress contributes to neck pain and back pain. When this tightness develops in the layer of muscles that cover the scalp, we call this a muscle contraction headache (or tension headache).

• *High blood pressure* — Prolonged stress can worsen high blood pressure in those who already have it, even though it does not seem to cause it. Stress can also intensify the effects that high blood pressure has on the body such as stroke, heart attacks, and peripheral vascular disease.

• *Heart disease (coronary artery disease)* — Stress is a risk factor for developing heart disease and can intensify the other risk factors that contribute to developing plaques within the arteries of the heart. This is serious business, as more American men and women die from heart disease than any other cause. For those who already have heart disease, stress can increase the frequency of chest pain, bring on a heart attack and worsen the outcome of heart attacks.

• *Migraine headaches* can be brought on by stress. Although the exact mechanisms are unknown, they seem to arise through the activation of nerves in the brain that, in turn, alter the activity of the blood vessels in the brain.

• *Immune system function* is altered by stress in many ways. People who are under long-term stress are more susceptible to viral infections, especially colds and flu, and can have a diminished response to the flu vaccine. In addition, stress can contribute to many autoimmune disorders, such as thyroid problems and flares of rheumatoid arthritis.

• *Bowel problems* are frequently linked to stress. People who have greater stress are more likely to develop a condition called irritable bowel syndrome and have long-term problems with constipation, diarrhea, abdominal pain and/or nausea.

• *Stomach ulcers* can be caused by sudden, severe, short-term stress, yet we do not fully understand how this happens. Many people who have ulcers have been shown to have an infection with a bacteria called Helicobacter pylori which can be treated with antibiotics. Some suspect that the immune dysfunction increases our susceptibility to this bacteria, but this has not been proven.

• *Anxiety disorders*, including panic attacks, can be worsened by prolonged stress. People who experience a severe trauma can develop a condition called post-traumatic stress disorder, which includes many symptoms of anxiety and panic attacks.

• *Sleep problems* are often caused by stress. If your body is in a state of arousal, you'll have a hard time falling asleep. You may also discover that you will awaken frequently, as stress can interfere with you body's ability to shift into a deep, restful sleep.

• *Exhaustion* occurs for many people under prolonged stress. Depending on your constitution, feelings of hopelessness, loss of control, or even depression can develop over time.

• *Sexual problems* can also develop from stress. We need to be relaxed in order for sexual interest and arousal to occur. If we are too agitated for our parasympathetic nervous system to function, we will have difficulty with the arousal phase of sex. In addition, stress can interfere with your closest relationships; this creates a barrier to intimacy as well.

I want to emphasize that stress is not the only cause of these problems. All illnesses are "multi-factorial," which means that there are many factors which contribute to the development of the disease. Stress works in combination with a person's genes, diet, environment and life experiences to produce a specific condition. It is not the only causative factor, but it is a very important one.

Are your symptoms stress-related?

In the traditional part of my medical practice, I rely on blood tests, X-rays and other diagnostic tests to tell me whether a person has a particular disease. In the behavioral part of my practice that addresses stress-related disorders, I ask the patients themselves to provide me with this information. We start by having them listen to their body. It often tells them what they need to know.

Let's do the same thing here. Consider this your own personal "house call." We'll start with the "Stress-Check Body Scan," which will help you to figure out where you hold stress in your body.

Stress-Check Body Scan

• Turn your attention to the muscles in your neck and shoulders. Is your neck stiff and sore? Are the muscles tightening so that your shoulders are drifting upward in the direction of your ears?

Try this: What would it feel like if you released the tension from them a bit, so that your shoulders drifted down and a bit toward your back?

•.What about your arms and your hands? Are you preparing to carry around the weight of the world, even as you sit reading? Are your hands tight, fists clenched, palms sweaty?

Try this: Can you let the tension release from your arms? Open your hands; allow them to rest loosely in your lap.

• Let your attention turn toward your face, especially around your forehead, your eyes and your jaw. Is there squinting, clenching or a frown? Do your eyes or scalp ache?

Try this: Soften the muscles of your face. Release your jaw slightly. Bring the corners of your mouth into a slight smile. How does that feel?

• Now focus on your chest. Is your breath shallow or rapid? Is it sometimes hard to get a full breath? Does your heart pound or beat quickly? Is the beat sometimes irregular so that you feel a flip-flop sensation?

Try this: Soften your belly so that when you breathe, the belly moves in and out. Slow your breathing a bit, allowing time for you to take a deeper breath. (Try not to get frustrated; this takes practice.)

• Next, focus on your abdomen, your belly. Is there indigestion, cramping or tightness? Do you feel like there is a "lead pit" in your stomach?

Try this: Focus on your belly as you change your breathing. Does anything soften in your belly?

• What about your back? Many people carry tension here, especially in the low back. Is it stiff or sore? Are you unable to bend over easily to pick things up without pain or strain?

Try this: Lie on the floor and bring your knees up to your chest, one at a time at first and then together. How does this feel?

• Finally, take a moment to turn inward and focus on your mood. How would you describe it? Restless, edgy or frustrated? Anxious, fearful? Sad, tired, hopeless?

Try this: Think about something you love. Take a full minute to dream about it, pretending that it is right there with you. Then check your mood. Any changes?

What did you discover? Where do *you* hold tension in your body? This body scan will give you a clue to where you are likely to develop illness and where you should focus to feel better and prevent disease.

Behavioral Stress Symptom Inventory

The next step is the Behavioral Stress Symptom Inventory. This will give you a sense of how your "way of being" in the world is affected by stress. As you take this test, think about how your family, friends or co-workers would answer these questions about you. Sometimes other people can see things about us that we can't see for ourselves!

Behavioral Symptoms

___Excessive smoking/   ___Grinding teeth at night
    gum chewing/eating   ___Inability to get things done
___Overusing alcohol
___Critical of others

Emotional Symptoms

___Crying   ___Easily discouraged
___Nervousness, anxiety   ___Edginess, ready to explode
___Mood swings, easily   ___Sense of immense pressure
    upset   ___Anger
___Boredom, no interest   ___Loneliness
    in things   ___Unhappiness for no reason
___Feeling like no one cares

Cognitive Symptoms

___Trouble thinking clearly ___Thoughts of running away
___Forgetfulness   ___Inability to make decisions
___Lack of creativity   ___Constant worry

___Memory loss ___Loss of sense of humor

Spiritual Symptoms

___Emptiness ___Feeling victimized

___Loss of meaning ___Loss of direction

___Doubt ___Cynicism

___Unforgiving

Relational Symptoms

___Isolation ___Blaming others

___Resentment ___Lack of intimacy

___Loneliness ___Fewer contacts with friends

___Lowered sex drive ___Bossiness

So What Can You Do About Stress?

In my experience, many people can improve their stress symptoms behaviorally. This means that by changing your behavior and your "way of being" in the world, you can change your reaction to difficult situations and ease the amount of tension you carry. The answers are actually quite simple. Simple measures that can make a profound difference.

"Simple?," you might ask. "If it was so simple, then why haven't I done this already? And why do we need an entire book discussing this?"

Then my response would be, "Simple, yes. But not necessarily easy."

"Oh," you might say. "I see. OK, I'm up for the challenge. I can do it. In fact, I'll probably do it faster than anyone else I know. I'm an expert at many things. Perfection is my middle name."

And then I would smile, compassionately, because I've been there (and still fall into that trap sometimes) and say, "That's the point. Peace is not actually anything that you achieve. It's something that you allow to happen."

Allow The Body to Heal

The most important way to heal from stress is to learn how to really relax your body. I don't mean sitting down and doing something relaxing like reading or watching TV. I mean learning how to bring your body into a state of relaxation and, in doing so, activate the parasympathetic nervous system on your own and use its power to release the stress from your body. This will allow your body to heal.

Medical research has explored this theory for more than 30 years. Repeatedly, studies have shown that any technique which activates the parasympathetic nerves will calm the body and mind to relieve acute stress symptoms. If these techniques are practiced regularly for 20 to 40 minutes a day, they will reduce the intensity of the body's reaction during stressful situations. Over the long-term, this will relieve the symptoms of stress-related diseases.

How can you activate your parasympathetic nerves? Relaxation training and meditation are good places to start. They are deep states of rest that are similar, but not identical, to that state when you are just beginning to fall asleep. Your body is quieter than if you were fully awake, and your mind begins to settle down as well. For those of you who are worriers, I imagine that this sounds wonderful. Every day I hear people say that they wish that they could quiet their mind, even if it was just for a few minutes!

There are many different ways of learning how to do this. Meditation practices, for instance, have you choose a "focus for your attention." This "focus" can be a word, phrase, prayer, or movement. The practice involves simply repeating these words (or movements) over and over for 20 to 40 minutes. For most people, a predictable sequence of events will happen. Your interest in this activity lasts for about five minutes. Then you become bored. Then the chatter in your mind (the thoughts, plans, worries, frustrations, etc.) becomes louder, making it harder to maintain your focus. But — if you stick with the practice, after a while you will notice that your mind becomes a bit quieter; your body begins to relax. The longer the practice session, the deeper the relaxation.

I know, it sounds simple. But anyone who has tried this knows that it is not easy. For many of us, the boredom or the chatter becomes so strong, we get frustrated and stop. Or, we begin to struggle with the chatter, hoping to force it to "Quiet down!" When this happens, our frustration rises and we lose our focus.

These responses are natural and reflect our "way of being" in this culture, which rewards our ability to think, plan, and do in order to achieve our goals. That's why meditation is hard. It asks us to learn a different way of being.

If you really want to use relaxation training or meditation to treat your stress-related symptoms, here are some tips.

• If you can, find someone who knows how to teach it. It's like learning how to ride a bike. You could read about it, but it's best to have someone actually teach you. If this is not an option, try using an audiotape. It's the next best thing to having someone with you.

• Try different techniques. Many people find that meditation is a difficult way to begin relaxation training. A practice which teaches progressive muscle relaxation or guided imagery is an easier way to start.

• Stretching and yoga are also wonderful ways to relax. When a muscle is stretched gently for 10-20 seconds, it sends a message through the nerves back to the brain and activates the parasympathetic nervous system. Even if your mind is chattering, the body is getting some stress-relief. Sometimes it's easier to focus on movement, so you could use stretching as a form of meditation by focusing on the muscles as they are stretched.

• Any type of aerobic exercise can also be a great stress reliever. If you want to combine the benefits of exercise and relaxation, turn your attention inward and focus on your breathing during your post-exercise cool down and stretch. Then give yourself another 15-20 minutes for meditation. You will be amazed at how deeply you can relax.

• It will be much easier to relax if you stop consuming caffeine and sugar. No, I'm not kidding. Caffeine works like adrenaline and creates a fight or flight reaction in your body. This will bring on more stress-related symptoms and make it harder to settle down during meditation or relaxation. If you crave the taste, try decaf. It contains stimulants other than caffeine but is a step in the right direction. Sugar also brings you up and down but in a different way. When you eat sugar, it is absorbed quickly. You feel a boost of energy — but only for a while. After the sugar high wears off, your blood sugar drops, leaving you feeling tired and irritable. You could chase this with more sugar, or you could use better quality food to help you feel well.

• If you fall asleep during meditation, it means that you aren't getting enough restful sleep at night. Commit to getting more sleep. Trouble falling asleep? Use relaxation training just prior to bedtime.

• Notice what happens in your mind during meditation. Frustrations or worries may arise, but when you choose to put these thoughts aside and return your focus to your relaxation, you develop a skill that you could use anytime to prevent yourself from reacting in the moment or carrying tension. It's not a long-term solution; it doesn't make the problem go away. But it can help you to put difficult situations aside until you are ready to resolve them more peacefully.

• My final tip is that you need to practice. My husband once asked an excellent guitarist how he got to be so good. "Practice," was his answer. This advice applies to any other skill. In my experience, it takes 3 to 4 weeks of a daily practice to begin to see the long-lasting benefits of relaxation training.

Some Final Words

You may find that despite your best efforts, you are still feeling poorly. That is the time to get additional help. See your doctor, have testing for other diseases, and consider herbs, homeopathy or medication if you need it. It doesn't mean that your self-care didn't work. It just means that the stress has impacted your body more severely than you can treat on your own.

Commit some time to take care of yourself and do it. I know that the world (and your company, and your family) needs you, but there are few things more important than your health. Even the airlines tell us to put on our own oxygen mask prior to putting on our children's mask. That's an important lesson to remember.

ABOUT
JANE SULLIVAN-DURAND, M.D.

Jane Sullivan-Durand, M.D., is a family physician with a mission: to help people take charge of their health by reducing their stress and to spread this word to the medical profession. In her innovative practice in Concord, New Hampshire, she sees individual patients and has developed a group process called It's Your Time To Be Well, *a program that has been adopted by other health professionals. She extended her practice into the field of cardiology and co-developed* Take Heart, *an aggressive heart disease treatment program. Individuals and professionals use her audiotapes for relaxation training.*

Dr. Sullivan-Durand's unique perspective arose from a personal health crisis that advanced her openness to different healing philosophies. In 1995, she suffered a serious complication from a medical procedure. After reaching an end-point in traditional medical care, she recovered successfully by utilizing alternative and complementary therapies. She advocates the use of non-traditional therapies and works with her husband, Lynn Durand, M.D., to explore how they may best be integrated with conventional medical care. Her near-death experience motivated her to make changes in her medical practice and her life. She is a dynamic and motivating speaker for health professional and lay audiences who want to hear new ideas for creating health.

Contact Information:
Jane Sullivan-Durand, M.D.
Center for Integrative Medicine
171 Pleasant Street
Concord, NH 03301
Phone (603) 228-7600
Fax: (603) 228-7320
E-mail: DrJane@drjane.com
Website: www.DrJane.com

Stress Hardiness or Stressed-Out: You Do Have a Choice

by Jamie Montelongo

The term "stress" is a relatively new word. It was first coined and studied in 1936 by Dr. Hans Selye. I am sure that stress was felt before that, probably since the beginning of time. Many articles and books say that one of the keys to becoming "stress hardy" is to think in an optimistic way. So let's give it a try.

What is the upside to stress? Well, one thing might be that when we are under stress we get a surge of adrenaline and other hormones that can give us a tremendous burst of energy. That really comes in handy when we are running for that bus, trying to hit a homerun, or grabbing for the last cashmere sweater at that end-of-season sale at our favorite department store.

But like a cousin who comes for a weekend visit and brings eight large suitcases, stress really becomes a problem when it stays longer than necessary. Sure, when we need to surge into our passing gear, stress causes a physical reaction that gives us a boost and supercharges us to take action. This is often referred to as the "fight or flight" response.

One time my family and I were flying to New York from Houston. We weren't stressed about our trip because we were looking forward to my brother-in-law's wedding. Not only was he marrying someone who would become one of my dearest friends, but it was an out-of-state wedding. That means that we didn't have to do anything but pack a nice change of clothes and show up. We were packed and ready to go, and even ahead of schedule! (Not the usual situation for me, but when it happens I feel pretty good about it.) Since we were early for our flight, why not stop at a diner for a bite to eat? It seemed logical at the time, so that is what we did.

While we were sipping our tea in a back booth, we heard a loud voice at the front of the diner. I stood up just to get a peek of what was going on, and to my surprise I saw a man with a large gun, his shirt wrapped around his head with only his eyes visible, standing at the register, yelling for all the money. He then nervously and in a threatening voice said to someone to his left, "Hey you, hang up that phone!" He then proceeded to shoot his big gun.

Speaking of shooting, that is exactly what my level of stress did... my stress shot through the roof! Immediately I pulled my three-year-old son down on the seat of the booth and covered him by lying over him. I asked him to be very quiet. My brother-in-law did the same with his two-year-old. My husband became quiet and super-alert, ready to spring into action if necessary. When the robber ran with his bag of money, my husband sprang into action. He made sure that the employees and customers were all right. He was the one that gave the directive to the stunned restaurant employees to call the police and lock the front door for safety's sake. The immediate stress we felt helped us to evaluate the situation and take safety measures. No one was hurt in this incident, but for a long time I could remember it and feel my stress level climb. Long after the event occurred, I could still feel real stress when calling it to mind or recounting the incident.

In spite of all this, we made it to the airport in plenty of time. But what I noticed was that my attitude had changed. I looked at people with suspicion. On previous visits to New York I had been impressed with the fact that New Yorkers were much friendlier than I had heard. Yes, on previous trips I had concluded that New York was a great place, with friendly people who walked fast and talked a little funny, but all in all were swell.

This trip for the wedding was different. What I felt walking down a New York street was threatened and a little fearful. I kept an extremely close eye on my son, even closer than usual. So what made this trip to New York very different from my visits before? Did I meet pleasant, helpful New Yorkers? Yes, I did. But my perception and focus had changed. Because of the recent diner robbery, I was concentrating on what might go wrong and what might present a danger to my family.

Like almost everything, there are upsides and downsides to stress. (Stressed spelled backwards is Desserts!) The trick is to get stress to work for us, not against us. The real danger to our health comes when we allow ourselves to become chronically stressed. The major diseases common to our culture, such as heart disease, high blood pressure, and cancer, are all stress-related illnesses.

What we need to remember is that stress is caused, not so much by situations, but by our own perceptions. Take for example my visits to New York City. Sometimes I met some really wonderful people. Sometimes I met some not-so-polite people. I had both positive and negative experiences each time I visited. What changed was my attitude and perception. If our thoughts can cause more stress, then the opposite is also true! The good news is that we can change and improve our perceptions, thoughts, and beliefs. Think about it . . . the really great news is that we can control our levels of stress!

Any workman needs the right tools to get a job done. If you were going to hang a picture on the wall, you would need specific tools. There are some simple and very effective tools that we should add to our inventory so that we effectively accomplish the rewarding job of becoming "stress-hardy."

Tool # 1: Positive Self-Talk

Whether you are Chatty Cathy or the Strong, Silent type, the odds are that the person with whom you do the most talking and communicating is yourself. How do you address yourself? Are you polite, kind, and forgiving? Or are you harsh, overly critical, and demanding? Has anyone ever asked you, "What are you smiling about?" Whether you choose to share that bit of self-talk or not, we all know that what we say to ourselves can cause our lips to turn up and our eyes to sparkle or can bring our emotions and mood crashing down.

Emotions manipulate our immune system by the chemicals and hormones we produce. If you often think negatively, then the hormones cortisol and adrenaline (just to name a couple) may suppress the healthy function of the immune system. Deeply rooted negative emotions can affect our health and well-being. Some people get into a habit of constantly looking at the downside. This has been called "awfulizing." Sometimes we play the "What if?" movie in our heads, and often we focus on the many things that might go wrong. Remember it is our movie! We get to write the script. If you paid to see a movie that you thought was awful, would you get up, walk out, and then ask for your money back? I hope you would. That is what I am asking you to do with your own mental movie. If you don't like the story line, then by all means get up, walk out, and change theatres.

At times we act and react in a way that is governed by long-term perceptions and beliefs that have outlived their usefulness. One time I had some friends over for dinner, including a man named Cy. I didn't know it when I planned the menu, but he absolutely hates squash of any kind, prepared in any way. I had cooked spaghetti squash in a rather unique recipe, which he ate and asked for seconds, and then ate that and proceeded to compliment the great meal. After learning he had eaten squash, Cy turned a shade of ghastly green and proceeded to become quite sick to his stomach. What made my dear friend so sick (as well as cautious about eating my cooking)?

I suspect that if he had not learned that he had eaten two generous helpings of squash, he would have been fine. He really believed that he hated squash, probably since he was a small child. He was truly, physically sick once he realized what he had ingested. Was it my cooking? I don't believe that for a moment! (Plus, no one else got sick.) Was it the taste? No, when someone takes a generous second helping, he isn't faking, but he really likes the taste of the food. So what made him turn and run for the hall bathroom? It was his belief that he hated squash and that eating it made him sick. Our perceptions, our beliefs, are really very powerful. Why not choose beliefs that give us the option of being stress-hardy and happy? We need to sniff out the beliefs that may be deeply rooted, long-standing perceptions that still affect our actions but have long ago outlived their usefulness.

Here are the helpful steps to vanquish negative, archaic thoughts and replace them with positive thoughts:

• *Identify* negative perceptions

What are you saying to yourself? It is for certain that people who are often depressed produce a lot of negative self-talk. Really listen to your self-talk. It may help to keep a journal of what you are saying. When you are feeling stress build and/or you start feeling depressed, take notes. Once identified . . .

• *Replace* the negative with positive self-talk

Don't argue with yourself. Just delete the negative, and replace it with a realistic and positive thought. Rather than beating yourself up about what went wrong, learn from the experience. Analyze what occurred, and immediately make plans to put this new knowledge to work to improve the situation.

For example, I have to admit that when my friend became ill after eating a meal I prepared, I had to fight the urge to take it personally. My first impression was to be embarrassed that after eating my food, one of my guests turned green and became ill. My first impression was to feel bad and say to myself, "Self, regardless of how nutritious and low in fat squash is, you should not have served it!" At that point I could have concluded that I would never buy or prepare squash again. But that was the moment to analyze. When I did, I realized that all my guests liked the meal. No one else got sick. Even Cy was bragging before he started gagging.

• *Don't take it personally*

We often tend to take situations personally when there is a bigger picture we need to see. The issue was not about my cooking, but about Cy's belief. He too had a choice. After eating a meal that he found to be very pleasing, then learning that he had eaten squash, he too had some options. One was to react just as he did. (That reaction does seem a little inappropriate at a dinner party, if you ask me.) Or he could have reasoned that his meal (1) tasted good, (2) was squash, and (3) that he must have been unfair in his long-standing vegetable evaluations. Maybe he could give squash another chance! Who knows, he might have found out that zucchini squash, summer squash, acorn squash, as well as spaghetti squash was something pleasant and desirable! (As well as nutritious and low in fat.) We really do have options here!

We can't always control what happens, but we can control our perceptions and attitudes. Our *attitude is more important* in determining how we handle stress, and even if we feel stress at all, *than what is the cause* of the perceived stress. Read that again. I really want you to remember this point.

Tool #2: Laughter

The more laughter and humor you have in your life, the less room you will have for stress. Physically, some amazing things happen when we laugh. Hardy laughter has been called "internal jogging." It really is exercise for our insides! Muscles tighten and then relax. Breathing becomes deeper, helping get oxygen into our bodies and helping us to feel better. Blood circulation increases. The digestive system improves. The body produces endorphins that help us feel and heal better.

Laughter and humor can go a long way in diffusing a stressful situation. Take, for example, our friend Tracy. Tracy is a fun-loving, big-laugh person who also happens to be weak in the department of "organization." Because of this she is known for running behind schedule most of the time. We have been known to invite our friends to join us for dinner, or a movie at 7:00 p.m., but Tracy gets her own special invitation for at least a half hour earlier. While we make allowances for Tracy, because she is so much fun, her boss is not nearly as flexible. Not long ago, Tracy received a warning, then a reprimand for being five to fifteen minutes late. Finally, she got an ultimatum that if she was late to work just once more, she would be fired. Tracy made extra effort for a week to get to work on time, even arriving early on a couple of occasions. We were all very proud of her but knew it was just a matter of time before another tardy occurred. We had a severe south Texas rainstorm one night, which caused a power failure, and Tracy's alarm clock failed her. She awoke late, and showed up at work a good 20 minutes behind schedule.

As she walked through the front door of her office, you could feel the tension as well as see it on the faces of her co-workers. They all knew what was coming. She was out of a job! Aware of her late arrival, her boss walked into the front office with a scowl on his face, completely ready to make good on his threat. Before he could say a word, Tracy spoke up. "Good morning Mr. Hamby. Is it true that the early bird gets the worm? I hear that there is job opening here and I just know that I can handle the work. Well, do I get the job?" Mr. Hamby's scowl didn't change, but he did turn around, walk back to his office and close his door, without asking Tracy to collect her personal items and leave. Her quick wit and ability to find humor did wonders in diffusing a very stressful situation.

It may help to practice "Joy Jotting." Why not take a couple of minutes at the end of your day to jot down some of the good things that have happened. Smile about them and go to sleep thinking of the blessings of your life. Remember, even the situations that do not go as we hope are valuable opportunities for us to learn, grow, become more empathetic, and do better the next time.

Tool #3: Love and Companionship

There was a story recounted at a business seminar dealing with human relationships. The speaker told of a home for orphaned babies. Inside this home was a long row where the babies were kept in their cribs. Some of these babies became ill and some of them died — except the baby in the last crib. This baby did better than expected. The doctor was perplexed. The care provided was consistent, since all were fed, bathed, and kept warm. Yet only the baby in the last crib thrived. As months passed and new babies were brought in, the story remained the same: Only the baby in the last crib did well. The doctor concealed himself to observe, so that he might find an explanation for the one child's robust condition.

At midnight the cleaning woman came in and on hands and knees scrubbed the floor, from one end to the other. After finishing her scrubbing, she stood up, stretched, rubbed her back. Then she went to the last crib, picked up the baby, walked around the room with it, cuddling it, talking to it, rocking it in her arms. She put it back in its crib and left. The doctor watched night after night, and each night the same thing happened. It was always the baby in the last crib that got picked up, cuddled, talked to, and loved. In all the new groups of babies brought in, it was always the baby in the last crib that thrived, while the others got sick and some died.

Psychology Today said that "during formative periods of brain growth, certain kinds of sensory deprivation — such as a lack of touching and rocking by the mother — result in incomplete or damaged development of the neuronal systems that control affection."

Loving, caring human relationships are vital to our health. Thus the opposite, the lack of companionship, can be detrimental. We are faced with many pressures in modern living, such as broken homes, single-parent families, emotionally neglected children, the mania for material things, the collapse of morals, the demise of true values — all add to the instability and loneliness that damage our health.

Many clinical studies support that there are medical consequences of loneliness. Humans have biological needs for love and human companionship, and the failure to meet these needs may be ultimately exacted in our own hearts and blood vessels. So what do you do if you find yourself feeling lonely? It is true that one may not have the love, support, and companionship biologically necessary for happiness, health, and stress-hardiness within the established relationships with our parents, our mates, or our children, but it is up to us to go out and create the relationships we need.

Get absorbed in something that is uplifting. Look to see what you can do within your own block, your own street, your own building. If you look you will find children who can benefit from your concern or a lonely person who is hoping for a friendship to be cultivated. Take action, and get to know an older person whose family lives far away, who could use a friendly visit or help of some kind.

The point is that love and companionship are essential to humans. When we have it in abundance, our stress is reduced. An example of this occurred in the town of Roseto, Pennsylvania. There was a very low death rate from coronary heart disease. The epidemiologists conducting the study expected to find a community of physically active, non-smoking, nutritionally conscious individuals. They got a big surprise! The people in Roseto had basically terrible health habits and were found to be high in the risk factors for heart disease. But they did have a major protective factor in their favor. It was found to be the social environment of the community. There was a large, extended family atmosphere there. People tended to grow up there and stay there to begin their own lives. There was a great deal of support and connection. Within the community, when a problem arose, people were available to help out, listen, and show concern. The study also showed that when people moved out of Roseto, their rate of heart attack rose to the predictable level. Connection, love, and social support proved to be more important than health habits in predicting heart disease.

As mentioned before, we need to snuff out the beliefs that may be deeply rooted and long-standing perceptions that still affect our actions but have long ago outlived their usefulness. So how can we overcome conditioning that causes us to close down in fear rather than be open to feelings of love, connection, and trust? Again we need to (1) identify our negative thoughts and (2) replace them with positive self-talk. One very effective way to counter stress is to cultivate an attitude of openness to love and forgiveness to ourselves and to others.

Tool #4: Before There was Prozac there was Massage

In a stress filled, technological society, we all seem to be running at cyber speed. We are designed to run in passing gear for only so long. Eventually, our bodies send us the message to slow down and lighten up. So many of today's major illnesses are stress related. Our bodies are wonderful and will heal and serve us well if we make it our priority to take control and make sure that we have the time, space, and environment we need to heal and counter the negative effects of stress. One of the oldest, safest, and most valuable therapies is Touch Therapy, or therapeutic massage.

Every living creature has a desire and a biological need to be touched. Touch is as essential to our health and welfare as is food and water. Massage therapy is an ideal remedy for stress because it fulfills our need for appropriate touch. Massage chemically sends a message to the body to slow down and relax. With this relaxation comes a sense of wholeness and serenity, and as our level of stress recedes, the immune system is better able to do the job of keeping us healthy. Therapeutic touch helps us listen to and understand the messages that our body is sending. Once we hear our bodies' messages, we can respond by making needed changes to get rid of that headache, slow down, create some alone time, or just make it a point to breathe deeply and get needed rest.

I recommend not letting one month go by without getting a massage. It is true that massage is an investment of time and money. It is also an investment in our own emotional and physical health. When you respect yourself enough to spend the time and money to get a massage, you are sending a message to the brain that you have value and worth. Remember, this is the only body you are going to get. Take care of it so that it will take care of you! Get a massage. You deserve it!

Ask people you know if they can recommend a good massage therapist. Visit several, and then choose one with whom you will feel comfortable. Or contact the International Massage Association (IMA) or the American Massage Therapy Association (AMTA) for therapists working in your area.

Many companies are offering regular massage as an employee benefit. Seated-massage, onsite at the workplace, is an effective and low-cost way of helping employees deal with job-related stress. Some of the benefits are listed below.

Massage does the following:

1. Reduces the physical and mental effects of stress, thus helps prevent burnout and stress-related illnesses

2. Relieves the adverse effects of sitting for long periods of time in the same position

3. Relieves physical problems associated with repetitive tasks, i.e., computer work, sorting, filing, and assembly line tasks

4. Improves alertness and ability to focus

5. Helps relieve common problems such as tension headaches, and stiff and sore muscles

6. Improves immune system functioning for better general health and resistance to colds and other illnesses

7. Leaves one feeling revitalized and ready to return to work

Determine to be stress hardy rather than stressed-out. It is your choice. The upside of stress is that it is a signal to examine the events taking place in your life. Look at your priorities, internal self-talk, beliefs, and the way you treat yourself. Search for areas in your life to simplify and embrace the values that are most important to you. Remember to laugh! Treat yourself and others with kindness and respect. As a massage therapist, I love my work and clearly see the benefits that therapeutic massage brings to my clients and myself. Make room for regular massage in your life. Consider massage therapy not an indulgence, but an investment in your long-term well-being. Make the choice to give stress a rest!

ABOUT
JAMIE MONTELONGO

Jamie Montelongo is a registered massage therapist and owner of Touchstone Massage Therapy Clinic. She specializes in therapeutic massage and trigger point therapy for pain and stress relief. Her areas of expertise include pregnancy massage and pain relief therapy for people with fibromyalgia. Jamie is certified in prenatal and peri-natal massage and is a certified lactation educator from the University of California at Los Angeles. One of Jamie's special interests is stress relief education. Jamie lives in San Antonio with her stressed out husband (!) and two sons.

Contact information:
Jamie Montelongo
Touchstone Massage Therapy
4118 McCullough Avenue
Suite 7
San Antonio, TX 78212
Phone: (210) 822-2848
Fax: (210) 494-3882
Email: JMontelongo@juno.com

Put Your Conversations into a "Stress Reliever Box"

by Mark Hunter

All of us have felt, at one time or another, that we would have far less stress in our lives if only everyone else thought and acted like us.

Sure ... you've thought this at least once in your life. In fact, on some days, you've thought about it hourly, especially when people just don't seem to be responding the way you want them to. It happens to all of us. It might be with a colleague at work, a superior, or the new employee.

Outside of a work setting, we experience this feeling frequently with children (teen-agers are excluded, as they are temporarily residing on another planet) or maybe with your spouse or a friend with whom you are having a simple conversation. If you think it hasn't happened to you, just remember the last time you asked someone to put something away or find something for you. What happened? Maybe they didn't put the item or items away the way you wanted them to. Or, maybe they actually located an item different from the one you wanted.

You see, we know what we want to say, and we know that we want the person we're talking with to remember what we're saying. More importantly, we know what it is we want the person to remember or do as a result of what we say. Yet, too many times, what that person perceives from what we are saying is far different from what we believe it should be.

No matter how simplistically we think we have conveyed our message, we find ourselves frustrated that the person we're talking to doesn't hear and understand the message the way we want. As a result of what we believed should have been a very simple conversation, we find ourselves walking away from the interaction with a feeling of stress. This stress, stemming from a feeling of being misunderstood, is then added to the other stress already in our lives.

No Time To Talk

All of this confusion is a direct result of the fast pace we are living and is compounded by the number of people we come in contact with and the brevity of time we have to spend with them. We are all victims of this time crunch and of not having enough time to communicate well with others. The end result is a breakdown in the conversations we do have and in the content of those conversations.

This habit of short-circuiting our conversation only adds to the level of stress emerging from many of the conversations we have. This short-circuiting occurs whether they take place in person, over the phone, via the Internet, or any other means we use to communicate. The remedy? We need to remember why we are having a conversation.

A conversation is a means for people to convey information, emotions, or feelings. The reason we find stress emerging from many of our conversations is simply because conversation is based on words. Today's language allows so many different interpretations of even one word that it is no wonder people don't always understand what we're saying. We all think we know the meaning of words. Yet, when we try to interpret what the other person is saying, it's easy to see why messages aren't always understood correctly.

The desired outcome of any conversation is for the people involved to understand what the message "means." However, because of the speed at which many of our conversations occur, we don't take the time to determine if what we're saying, and the way we're saying it, is really being understood. This short-circuiting is a direct result of our tendency to believe that everyone we have a conversation with thinks the way we do and will understand what we're saying.

To gauge the impact of multiple interpretations, let's look at a simple example. Just think of the words, "Where's the restroom?" When someone asks you this question, does it mean that person is merely looking for directions for future reference? Does it mean the person needs to find the restroom right away? Or could it possibly mean he or she really expects the other person to serve as a guide to the actual location? You can see that even a few simple words can have multiple interpretations. Of course, in this case, it would be natural to observe the questioner's body language and listen to vocal tone to determine the urgency of the question. Yet, the person asking the question doesn't necessarily know how the other person will respond. If responses can be so varied on a simple question like this, you can see how mixed up a more complicated conversation could become.

To help reduce the stress that occurs from misinterpreted messages in conversations, we need to step back and re-think how a typical conversation occurs. Usually, a conversation consists of two people who are exchanging information through a series of comments made by either or both of the people. Sounds simple enough. Where's the problem?

The problem is that we make the mistake of thinking a conversation is "good" anytime we get some sort of a response or comment out of the person we're talking to. We think because they asked a question or added a comment to what we said that they truly understood what we were saying. It is this assumption that the other person understands what we were saying — based on nothing but a comment from that person — that gets us into trouble. Our quick assumption is then compounded into stress when we find out, after the fact, that the person we've spent time talking to actually interpreted the conversation differently.

The Conversation Box

The best way for us to re-think how we have a conversation is by visualizing an image or a picture. Having a picture in our mind makes it easier for us to stay focused on what we want to say by only having to associate what we're saying with the image. For this process it's best to visualize a box, one with four equal sides.

A box is a convenient way to store or carry something. But if the box does not have a lid securely in place, the contents of the box will immediately fall out if we turn the box over. Now think of each side of the box as part of the conversation and the conversation itself is placed inside the box for the other person to carry away. Just like the object that falls out when the box is turned upside down, the conversation we have with another person will "fall out of the box" as soon as it is finished, and the meaning of it will be lost forever if we don't secure the box. When this loss occurs, we find ourselves having the same conversation with the same person all over again, hoping the second time we will see better results than the first time.

Our challenge is to have a discussion on a subject only once with a person and, in turn, minimize the stress that occurs from having the same conversation multiple times. We can only hope to achieve this when we view our conversation as something that is to be placed in a box and, more importantly, a box with a lid. Only when we have a conversation in this manner — when we have taken the time to put a lid on the box and close it securely — can we achieve the desired results from the conversation.

Using our picture of a box with four sides, we can then break down our conversation into four distinct parts. Each part of the conversation contributes to the total success of the conversation, ensuring that everyone fully understands what is being said and what can or should be done based on what has been said. Each side of the box is equally important and, like a real box, if one side is damaged or weakened, the integrity of the entire box is at risk. You would never think of storing something important in a box that had a large hole in one side or one side torn off. Likewise, a conversation that is missing a part is equally inadequate.

Think of a conversation you have had recently. Now, picture the square box with four sides, with each one of the four sides representing another part of the conversation. Choose either the left or right side of the square box and think of that as the beginning of the conversation — the essence of what you want to say. Now, consider the bottom of the box as side two. Since it is the floor of the box, this will represent where the information you are sharing is being stored. The third side of the box is the natural exchange of comments between you and the person you are talking to, as questions arise or additional comments are made. This is the point in the exchange where the nature of the conversation changes, and we begin to have a different type of conversation.

Most people mistakenly stop the conversation here. We have an assumption that, because there has been a *dialogue* between both parties, then everything is understood correctly. Two elements contribute to this assumption: 1) lack of time to continue the discussion, and 2) our belief that everyone thinks the same way we do. So what occurs? The subject of the conversation has been placed into the box, but the box — and the conversation — lacks a lid. Without a lid, the content and meaning of the conversation will be lost when the box is "tipped."

Tipping Over the Box

Although no one will intentionally tip the box over, it will tilt or fall on its own, due to the pace of daily activity we all find ourselves caught up in. "Tipping" will occur because, during the conversation, we failed to make certain that the person we talked with truly understood what we were talking about. We also failed to share the message in a way that would be remembered.

In addition, what happens to the other person after our conversation is, of course, beyond our control. The person carrying the box with our shared conversation will encounter another person, and another conversation will begin. Then they'll have another conversation in another box (probably without a lid) to juggle . . . or they might simply put the second conversation into the box with the first one. Or they'll start another activity. Whatever happens next, the result will be the same —

without even realizing it, the original box will be "tipped" and the contents lost forever.

Without our even realizing it, all the effort we put into a conversation can be suddenly lost, either through our neglect or the neglect of the person we spoke with. And, worst of all, we don't even know the contents of the conversation are lost until it's too late. Is there any wonder we find ourselves repeating many of the conversations we have already had, or why we find ourselves with stress in our lives due to the conversations we attempt? It is all due to the fact that too many of our conversations don't include the final step: placing a lid on the box.

Our final step in a conversation should be putting a lid on the box — adding the fourth and final side of our box. This is, by far, the most difficult part of any conversation. Yet it is without a doubt the most important. We naturally tend to think of ourselves as being better at communicating than most people, and we assume the person we're talking to really does understand what we're talking about. To get us over this hurdle, we need to check for understanding as part of our conversation. No . . . we don't have to ask the person we've been talking with to complete a test on what we said. However, in a roundabout way that is what we're doing with the lid of the box. We're asking questions that measure not just the other person's level of understanding, but also that person's ability to use the information. We do this by asking questions in a way that challenges the person to think about and play back to us what the information means and how it might be used.

Knowing the Score

Think for a moment of a major college football game. After the game, how do we know who won and who lost? We know who won and lost because of the score. If we weren't able to watch the game, we could always look at the score to learn the outcome — and sometimes, from the score alone, we can even determine if the game was good or bad.

Now, can you imagine two college teams taking the field to play a major game and, just moments before the game starts, the coaches decide not to keep score? If that were ever to occur, can you imagine what the fans, sportswriters, and players would say? There is no way the game would have the same intensity without a score. In fact, most of the fans present for the game would probably leave before the game started. You can quickly imagine how, after the game, each team's players and fans would claim victory based on what they saw. Each side would use various parts of the game or key plays to lay claim to beating the other team. In fact, you would probably hear both sides talking about the same play or plays and both making arguments that their team won the game based on those plays.

Just as ridiculous as not keeping score in a big game, many of our conversations don't have a finish — a lid. When we fail to place a lid on our conversations, we have essentially just played a game without keeping score. The outcome? Just like in a football game without score-keeping, people would be making all kinds of interpretations based on their own individual perspectives. Is there any wonder why we have to repeat so many of our conversations or why people misinterpret what we're saying? Is there any wonder we have stress in our lives due to conversations that don't result in the outcomes we want?

This conversation lid is like the score of the football game. This is where we determine, without a doubt, if what we've said makes sense to the person we're talking to. The key to this step is to be able to ask questions in a manner that neither insults the person's intelligence nor puts them into an uncomfortable situation. If we do either, we risk never being able to have a meaningful conversation with that person again. Rather, we need to ask a question or make a statement that stimulates their thinking and builds on each side of the conversation that has taken place.

Your goal with the lid is two-fold. First, you want to make sure that the person you are talking to understands and interprets what you've said in the same way you meant it. Second, and most important, you want the person to be able to use what you've said in the way you intended. Placing a lid on the conversation is your way of ensuring the conversation is connecting.

The Conversation Box in Action

Some examples of how this might work are as simple as asking for clarification, as in the "Where's the restroom?" example mentioned earlier. If you are asking the question, and the person you ask says something like, "They're down the hall and on the right," you might ask if the men's and women's restrooms are in the same area, or if they are across from one another. This is a way of simply and politely asking them to think once again of the location of the restrooms to ensure what they told you is correct. If you need to use the restrooms in an emergency and you ask, "Where's the restroom?" you might follow up with another question, such as "Are there usually long lines of people waiting?" This second question now places a little stronger sense of urgency on what you initially asked and may encourage the person you're asking to think through the answer to guide you to the best restroom to use in this circumstance. Although both of these examples are very simple, you can see the variances in understanding that might occur in even the simplest conversation.

Now let's begin to use these steps in a more complex conversation, one that may occur in a workplace between two colleagues where there is no direct reporting relationship.

Picture an office hallway where people are talking about an upcoming meeting and the expectations that various people will be bringing information to the meeting to update the others. In this situation, two colleagues are discussing the upcoming meeting, and one begins to tell the other what information his team will bring and what he expects the other person and his team to bring. After sharing a few key facts on what the first team will bring, the first person then casually states, "I assume your team will be bringing charts 'B' and data 'C' to the meeting." The other person acknowledges that is what his team will bring, and he goes on to say that, because the data is laid out so well, it will complement what the other team is bringing, so the meeting will be over early.

Following the normal path of rushed communication, the conversation would normally end at this point, and both parties would show up at the meeting with their information. Yet, to their dismay, they realize that the information each brings conflicts with data provided by the other. This outcome occurs because both parties failed to put a lid on the conversation by asking one another for clarification and application. An example of putting a much-needed lid on the conversation might have been for one party to take the conversation one step further. It might be with a statement followed by a question, such as: "We'll be sharing our facts that will show a major financial risk exists with the project. It would seem like the data you've been working with should show how we could save some money and reduce the risk. What does your data show?"

This example shows that, by making a statement and asking a question at the same time, the second party will now think about what his team is going to bring to the meeting and, more importantly, the contents of the data. The end result of capping the conversation with this type of statement/question? The other party is forced to respond verbally, and an additional opportunity is created to further the dialogue without making anyone feel uncomfortable or threatened. Both parties then leave the conversation with an understanding of what is expected — from both parties — for the upcoming meeting. The outcome is less stressful on both parties, as they have a much better feeling for how the meeting will turn out.

Making Your Conversations Work

The key to the example above is, first, for you to picture yourself in the type of conversation you have on a regular basis. Most people, by the very nature of their personality and the type of occupation they're in, tend to have the same types of conversations again and again. Begin to develop some questions and statements that you can use on a regular basis — questions that are probing in nature and statements that call for a response. Remember, the goal is not to put yourself onto a pedestal or to boost your ego by putting other people down. Rather, the goal is for both parties to leave the conversation with a much better understanding of what has been said and, more important, how it will be applied. This portion becomes the fine art of making good conversation, as it sets the tone for how the next conversation will go with this person. If you're the type of person who uses conversations as a sporting-event in a manner that declares a winner or loser, you'll find yourself with another problem. This time your problem may not be in putting a lid on the current conversation but in ever having a meaningful conversation with the person again. Yes, you will be able to have a conversation; however, it runs the risk of becoming extremely defensive in nature. This in turn will create an additional barrier that must be overcome when attempting to put a lid on a conversation.

Making the Box a Habit

The fine art of communication and putting the all-important lid on your conversations does take practice. But the outcome will be a reduction in the stress that is created from misunderstandings, misinterpretations, and continuously feeling that you have to repeat previous conversations. Key items to remember are to always visualize the box and the need to place a lid on any conversation you have. Placing the lid on the box means asking for clarification and application of what you've said. This means you don't ask for people to respond to what you've said; that typically is clarification in its most basic form. The key is in asking for application; in this regard you're asking for people to demonstrate back to you exactly how they will use the information.

To aid you in applying this tactic, draw a square on your to-do list for the next 21 days. The square will serve as a reminder to use this tactic when having a conversation. The square also serves as a second tool. Each day you need to mark in the middle of the square the concept behind a conversation you had the day before, in which you used the technique. Additionally, you should record the question and/or statement you used to place a lid on the conversation and how the person responded. Keeping the square visually in front of you for a period of 21 days will help make it a habit. Recording what you said to place a lid on the conversation will serve as an evaluation tool to gauge your effectiveness.

The true test of the box technique comes over a period of time when you're able to see how time has impacted conversations you've had and what people have done with them over time. Only time will tell how effective you are in placing a lid on conversations. In the end, the amount of stress you remove from your life as a result of this technique will be in direct proportion to the quality of the lid you create. Go ahead and starting building your lids. The only thing you have to lose is stress.

ABOUT
MARK HUNTER

Mark Hunter works with people and companies helping them present their messages more effectively. He offers consulting, seminars and keynote speeches.

Mark spends more than 100 days a year traveling, working with companies and individuals. From corporate boardrooms to small town sales calls, Mark's communication strategies make a difference in people's lives. The foundation for his work is 25 years of management experience. He knows exactly what it takes to communicate effectively with many types of people in various situations. Beginning with managing a fast-food restaurant at the age of sixteen, to spearheading the building of a 900-person sales team for a major corporation, Mark has held leadership positions in three multi-national corporations. Mark's extensive background in sales and marketing leadership enables his strategies to be on target with today's environment.

Contact Information:
Mark Hunter
MJH & Associates
15633 Underwood
Omaha, NE 68118
Phone: (402) 445-2110
Fax: (402) 445-0942
E mail: MarkJHunter@email.msn.com

Getting Into *Stress Shape*

by Laurie Richards

You probably know someone who has gone through a divorce, sent her kids off to college, got promoted, and held it together. And you probably know someone who can break a fingernail and fall apart.

What kind of *Stress Shape* are you in?

Stress in our lives is not going away. In fact, if you believe the experts, it can be expected to increase.

Surviving — even thriving — in business and at home is not dependent on eliminating stress, but on our ability to function effectively within the stress we're experiencing.

The ability to manage stress is determined, in great part, by the condition you are in to handle it — your *Stress Shape*. You can get into shape for stress, similar to the way you can condition yourself physically.

The Fundamentals of *Stress Shape*

Admit that life happens. Challenging situations are going to continue to happen. Children grow up and leave. Others get promotions that you want. Parents criticize. Spouses demand. Companies change direction. Traffic backs up. People change. We make mistakes. Life happens. Individuals in good *Stress Shape* understand that it is not what happens to a person, but how he responds to it that determines success in life, in work, and in relationships.

Make choices. In every situation in life, we have choices. We can accept things as they are. We can change our attitudes and/or our behavior. We can leave the situation. We may not like those choices, but they are our choices to make. Ignoring those choices, blaming others, and surrendering to fate only increase our stress. Those in strong *Stress Shape* make choices without blaming others. They make changes in their own behavior and attitudes without expecting others to change. They recognize that indecision is, in fact, a decision to accept.

Take strategic action. As human beings, we are creatures of habit. Our alarms go off the same time every day. We reach over and hit that snooze the same number of times. We go to work, stopping at the same coffee shops, having the same flavored coffee fixed the same way. We listen to the same radio stations, read the same newspapers, and watch the same television shows. The question is: Do these activities serve you? Or are you doing them just because you've always done them?

Strategic action means looking at where you are — and where you're going. Then asking, "What do I have to do to get there?"

Want to build *Stress Shape*? Start taking action that leads you in the direction you want to go. People in good *Stress Shape* recognize when they're on the wrong road and get off. They change direction based on their desired outcome.

Move on. Everyone makes mistakes. People in good *Stress Shape* learn from those mistakes and use the experiences to propel them to the next level. On the other hand, people in poor *Stress Shape* focus on the past, second-guessing and blaming themselves and others for everything from heartache to job loss to crashes on Wall Street.

Be self-interested. If you don't take care of yourself, you won't have the time, energy, or ability to take care of others. Building *Stress Shape* requires a commitment to self-interest, taking time for yourself, nurturing yourself, respecting yourself, listening to yourself, paying yourself first.

Keep proper perspective. How bad is it? Really? Individuals in strong *Stress Shape* understand the need to keep proper perspective. For instance, the scratch on the new car. It was going to happen someday. Right? Your son's blue hair. It could be worse. He could be on drugs or on the streets. Your daughter's pregnant. What's more natural than two young people making love? At least she has you to count on for support. Right? Some idiot driver cut you off in traffic. He could have run into you. He's now all of one car length ahead of you. Big deal. Individuals in *Stress Shape* live by the popular saying, "Don't sweat the small stuff — and it's all small stuff."

Using the information in this chapter, you can determine your *Stress Shape* by measuring three areas: situational experiences, physical condition, and psychological disposition. Then you'll be able to develop a personal training program designed to get you into stress shape.

Four steps to getting the most out of this chapter:

1. Measure your *Stress Shape* by taking the self-assessments for all three areas;
2. Identify your trouble-spots: situational, physical, or psychological;
3. Develop your *Personal Training Regimen,* setting specific goals to strengthen your trouble-spots;
4. Persevere.

Step One: Measuring Your Stress Shape

There are three areas that determine your *Stress Shape* — the stress you'll competently handle in your life:

1. Situations you're experiencing;
2. Physical health, strength and endurance;
3. Psychological disposition.

Situations

Identify which of the following events you have experienced within the past 12 months. If you have experienced the situation more than once, multiply the corresponding score by the frequency of the event.

Situation	*Score x Frequency = Score*
Death of spouse or close friend	100
Divorce or separation	73
Jail term	63

Situation	Score x Frequency = Score
Personal injury or illness	53
Marriage	50
Fired at work	49
Marital reconciliation	45
Retirement	45
Injury or illness of partner/family member	44
Pregnancy	40
Sex or conception difficulties	39
Gain of a new family member	39
Business re-organization/new boss	39
Change in income	38
Increase in personal debt	38
Career change	36
Mortgage of more than $100,000	31
Foreclosure of mortgage or loan	30
Change in work responsibilities	29
Child leaving home	29
Trouble with in-laws	29
Outstanding personal achievement	28
Change in spouse or partner's work	26
Begin or finish school	26
Change in personal habits	24
Trouble with boss	23
Change in work hours or conditions	20
Residential move	20
Change in school	20
Change in recreational activities	19
Change in church activities	19
Change in social activities	19
Mortgage or loan less than $100,000	17
Change in sleeping habits	16
Change in eating habits	15

Situation   *Score x Frequency = Score*
Vacation 13
Christmas celebration 12
Minor law violations 11
TOTAL   _____

Physical Condition

Using the following scale to measure your physical condition.

Strongly Agree = 1   Somewhat Disagree = 4
Agree = 2   Disagree = 5
Somewhat Agree = 3   Strongly Disagree = 6

___ I eat a healthy diet.

___ I limit my caffeine intake to three servings a day.

___ I drink adequate water (6-8 glasses per day).

___ I get seven to eight hours of sleep at least four nights a week.

___ I have a healthy sex life.

___ I know my cholesterol level, and it is healthy.

___ I exercise at least 20 minutes at least three times a week.

___ I do both aerobic exercise and strength building exercises.

___ I am at an appropriate weight (no more than 15 percent over or underweight).

___ I am in overall good health (eyes, teeth, hearing, etc.)

___ I don't smoke.

___ I limit alcoholic beverages to no more than two per day.

___ I do not abuse drugs (prescription or illegal).

___ My income is adequate to provide food, shelter, and clothing.

___ I have at least one reliable relative within 50 miles.

___ I get strength from my spiritual beliefs.

___ I am socially active.

___ I have a network of good friends.

___ I have a pet.

___ I am able to express my emotions appropriately (anger, fear, worry, love, etc.)

___ I have appropriate conversations with the people I live with about chores, household budget, and other living issues.

___ I do something fun at least once a week.

___ I laugh at least five times a day.

___ I regularly take time for myself.

___ I get an annual physical exam.

___ I have the physical exams appropriate for my age and gender (colonoscopy, prostate, mammogram, etc.)

___ I've had my eyes checked within the past 12 months.

___ I've had my teeth cleaned within the past 12 months.

___ I have visited my dentist within the past 12 months.

___ TOTAL SCORE

Psychological Disposition

Check any statements that describe your beliefs. Then tabulate your score using the formula below.

___ Trying my best at work makes a difference.

___ If it's going to be, it's up to me.

___ Having a lot to choose from is stimulating and exciting.

___ Opportunity is more important than security.

___ The average citizen can make a difference.

___ I enjoy variety in life, diet, schedule, etc.

___ I understand where I'm headed in life.

___ Getting ahead takes good luck and the right breaks.

___ Trusting fate is all I can do to make a relationship work.

___ Having a lot to choose from is frustrating and difficult.

___ Security is more important than opportunity.

___ One person can make little, if any, difference.

___ I prefer to stick to a routine and schedule.

___ I tend to live by habit, not by design.

____ I understand the part I play in helping my organization reach its goals

____ I'm good at what I do at work.

____ I enjoy a strong personal relationship.

____ I'm comfortable being alone with myself.

____ I'm responsible for where I am physically, financially, in my career, and in my relationships.

____ I just do what I'm ask to at work.

____ I'm not certain how I'm doing at work.

____ Having close relationships is risky.

____ I'm not comfortable being alone; I'd rather be busy.

____ I'm the way I am because of the way I grew up and how others have treated me.

____ TOTAL SCORE

____ TOTAL SCORE

Subtract the total number of checks in column B from the number of checks in column A for your final score.

$$\underline{\hspace{3cm}} - \underline{\hspace{3cm}} = \underline{\hspace{3cm}}$$

Column A   *minus*   *Column B*   *equals*   *Final Score*

Step Two: Identifying Your Trouble-Spots

Using the following guidelines, identify your trouble-spots.

Situations:

A score of less than 150 indicates that you are experiencing few stressful situations in your life. You are dealing with normal day-to-day frustrations, celebrations, and stresses.

Recommended action: Life is going to happen. Situations are going to crop up. Count your blessings that you didn't have to deal with more of them.

A score of 150-300 indicates that you are experiencing several stressful situations. You've had considerable life changes in the past 12 months that could lead to a vulnerability in your *Stress Shape.*

Recommended action: You're in the middle of the action. Looking for the things you can control within these situations before — and as

— they occur will help you compensate and build your *Stress Shape*. In the meantime, letting go of the aspects that you cannot control will help you navigate through the stress.

A score of 301+ indicates that you are experiencing a great deal of stressful situations. You've encountered significant life changes in the past year that may be leading to increased vulnerability in your *Stress Shape*.

Recommended action: You're changing at warp speed. Start building your *Stress Shape* by gaining some perspective. Start by asking yourself some key questions. How perfect do things need to be? What's the worst thing that can happen? What's the best thing that can happen? In the scheme of things, how important are some of these situations? Can I change them? How can I learn something from this? Where's the good in this?

Let go of things you can't control.

There is good news. First, the more you experience, the easier it becomes to handle the next life-changing event. Second, a strong score in the Physical or Psychological areas will quickly help you overcome any vulnerability generated by these situations.

Physical

A score of 29-59 Congratulations. Your body is working for you as a strength-building tool. You understand that you cannot take care of others unless you have taken care of yourself.

Recommended action: Keep up the good work. Continue your healthy lifestyle. You can be confident that, when challenging situations arise — as they will — you will be well-equipped to handle them.

A score of 59-126 You have some good lifestyle habits — and some not-so-good ones. You may notice the occasional backache, headache, upset stomach, etc., in times of high stress. Just what you don't need.

Recommended action: You have an incredible stress-strength-building tool right under your nose . . . literally. Start making choices about what you do with your body. It can work for you — or against you. Make a choice and take action to support it. Make time for exercise, get to the doctor, eat right. You know what to do. Do it and you'll be in good *Stress Shape* before you know it.

A score of 127-175 Your body is actually working against you as a strength-building tool. In fact, it may be the cause of much of your stress. You're undoubtedly experiencing recurring stress symptoms including backaches, headaches, ulcers, over-indulgence, etc. Keep doing this, and things will get worse.

Recommended action: Of the three areas (situation, physical, psychological), this one is exclusively under your control. Question your choices in times of stress. Are you reaching for chocolate or broccoli? Are you exercising or having a cocktail? Are you ignoring signs of ill-health and avoiding your physician, or are you diagnosing early and practicing prevention?

Psychological disposition

A score of -8 to 0 You seem to believe that you have very little control over your life. In fact, you may blame your parents, family, boss, government, and others for your station in life. You may have actually surrendered to fate and chance. The good news: it's not over until you decide that it's over.

Recommended action: Recognize that it's not your mother's fault that your hips are big. It's not your spouse's fault that your relationship is falling apart. It's not your boss's fault that you're not getting ahead. Get ready to answer the tough questions.

1. What could I have done differently and gotten different results?
2. What am I ignoring that could improve my situation?
3. What do I pretend not to know that is hurting me?
4. What should I have learned from previous experiences?
5. What should I have confronted earlier to prevent what is now a difficult situation?

A score of 0-8 You may believe that you are responsible for your position in life. You may not be acting on that responsibility. You may be afraid of acting for fear of the outcome. Sometimes it is easier to let someone else take the lead. But you can't ignore that you are accountable.

Recommended action: You are almost there. Work on exercising control over your life and face challenges head-on. Ask yourself if your fears are realistic? What's the price if you take action? What's the price if you don't? Which price would you rather pay?

A score of 8-12 Congratulations. You have accepted responsibility for where you are and see yourself as accountable for where you're going. You feel that you have control in your life and are committed to exercising that control. You appreciate a good challenge and have a hardy attitude when one arises.

Recommended action: Keep up the good work. Continue to exercise your control over your life to take you wherever you want to go.

Step Three: Developing Your Personal Training Regimen

Using the results of the three self-assessments, you can develop a Personal Training Regimen for getting into *Stress Shape* in three simple steps:

1. Choose three trouble-spots for alterations.

   a. Trouble-spots you want to *eliminate*: e.g. Smoking

   _____

   _____

   _____

   b. Areas you want to strengthen:
     e.g. Seeing the opportunity in tough times

   _____

   _____

   _____

   c. Trouble-spots you want to reduce:
     e.g. Saying "yes" when I mean "no"

   _____

   _____

   _____

2. Identify specific outcomes for each area.

a. I am eliminating smoking from my habits beginning April 12, 2002.

b. Effective immediately, when perceived negative situations happen, I actively search for the opportunities I can capitalize upon.

c. I assertively (not aggressively) say "no" when I mean "no."

3. Discover tools to help you attain those outcomes.

a. Research smoking cessation tools on the internet; discuss options with my doctor and pharmacist.

b. Ask others about potential opportunities and positive aspects of otherwise negative situations.

c. Using the internet and training resources, research an effective system for saying "no" without the added stress of guilt.

4. Take action.

a. Use smoking cessation techniques.

b. Discipline myself to look and find the opportunities.

c. Practice techniques for saying "no" when I mean it.
    i. Validate request
    ii. Say "no"
    iii. State a reason
    iv. Offer an alternative

5. Celebrate successes.

6. Monitor your progress.

7. Make it a habit.

a. Repeat action until it becomes more difficult to not use the techniques.

Step Four: Persevering

Six Tips for Persevering with Your Personal Training Program:

1. *Limit yourself* to three areas of improvement at a time. Trying to do it all is like trying to bench press 250 pounds when you are in shape for only 110 pounds. You'll hurt yourself!

2. *Be progressive.* Once you've mastered one area, choose another, strengthening and increasing endurance at every juncture. The way you get to the 10-pound dumbbell is by gradually increasing the weight — little by little.

3. *Be creative.* Find new opportunities and fresh ways of looking at people and situations.

4. *Try again.* Just because an idea didn't work for you six months ago doesn't mean it won't work for you today.

5. *Manage your expectations.* You can have it all, although you might have to change your definition of "all."

6. *Celebrate your small successes.* You wouldn't wait until you lost 50 pounds to celebrate. Successful dieters celebrate every five pounds. Assertively saying "no" deserves a pat on the back. Surviving a vacation with the in-laws may be worthy of a new set of golf clubs.

Good luck!

ABOUT LAURIE RICHARDS

*L*aurie Richards travels the world helping people become better managers and communicators. Described by international audiences as "enthusiastic, professional, effective, inspiring and enlightening," Laurie's Growing Morale and Stress Shape seminars are especially popular in today's fast-changing, multi-stressed society.

Laurie Richards worked as a reporter for Public Broadcasting, hosted her own television show, managed one of the nation's fastest growing public relations agencies, launched award-winning public affairs programs and managed highly effective grassroots lobbying programs. Today Laurie leads seminars and delivers keynotes that help many Fortune 500 companies and associations improve communication and leadership skills, which positively impact their bottom lines.

Additionally, she has coached hundreds of professionals for media interviews, legislative visits, lobbying efforts and presentations. Laurie has authored several books and educational audio and video programs including the best-selling Speaking Without Fear. She is the author of Communicating Charisma, Trust and Credibility.

Contact Information:
Laurie Richards
Laurie Richards & Associates
12 Purple Martin
Hackettstown, NJ 07840
Phone: (908) 813-3971
Email: ladrichard@aol.com

PUT A TWIST ON STRESS! BE FLEXIBLE!

by Jolene Carson, R.T., M.A.

Professionals face major stressors both at work and at home. Most of us are overly busy, juggling many responsibilities while trying, at the same time, to live a life of peace, joy, and fulfillment. Although we don't want to eliminate "*eustress*," the positive form of stress, we do want to control distress, negative stress. Even when the pressure is on, by being flexible we can reduce ineffective responses to stress while maintaining concentration, energy, and productivity.

To cope with high stress, one needs to balance the demands of work and personal life without sacrificing either. Stress in one area of life impacts other areas, and coping resources in one area can be used to reduce stress in another area. The key is in balance, which is essential for overall life satisfaction.

To reduce the negative effects of stress, you need to examine the sources of your stress. *What causes you stress?*

- Too much work and too little time?
- Changes at work?
- Changes at home?
- The "Hurry" Syndrome?
- Family demands?
- Waiting in long lines?
- Dealing with people?
- Deadlines?

- Traffic?
- The unknown?
- Other_____

Whatever the cause of your stress, you can find relief by being *flexible*. Have you ever been in a stressful situation and had someone say, "Now don't get bent out of shape." People read our body language, often before we realize the message that we're sending. Under stressful conditions, it's easy to lose our normal composure. Sometimes we exhibit behavior quite unbecoming to us and people can see that we are losing control. Yet, as the saying goes, "flexible people won't get bent out of shape."

Would you like to reduce your stress? It is certainly possible to change the way that you react to stress and thereby make life less stressful. We are going to talk about some simple yet effective techniques to help you be more flexible.

What is flexible? One of the definitions of flexible is: *adjustable to change*. To be flexible, one must use a way of thinking, a mental skill that promotes effective thinking and responding. It means having an appropriate attitude for the situation and making adjustments as necessary.

What does it mean to be flexible? To be flexible, one must realize that things are never the way that they seem. Things are a matter of perception and each one of us will have differences in our perception of a situation. In almost any stressful situation, some kind of change has taken place. If we are to deal with a stressful situation effectively, we must recognize the change and adjust to it.

Most of us have the ability to adapt to change; we just have to use our ability. Some other characteristics of flexibility include the following:

1. Be willing to adapt to change

2. Value others' points of view

3. Be open to new possibilities

4. Control worry

5. Change or modify your behavior as needed

6. Take good care of yourself

Now let's discuss each one of these individually.

1. Be willing to adapt to change

The key word here is *willing*; you may not need to change your ways or behavior for the event, but you must be open to the possibility.

- The first step is to realize that change has taken place.
- Following this awareness, it is important that you analyze the change. Some points to consider are:
  — What caused the change?
    ○ Is it due to normally occurring change/s?
    ○ Is there a new person or a new mix of people involved?
    ○ Is a new requirement (procedure, policy) being introduced?
    ○ Did something need to be fixed?
  — Is the change completely out of your hands?
  — Can you see how it might possibly be beneficial?
- Then determine if perhaps you could get a better outcome if you made a change.
  — If you are willing to adapt, it will be much easier for you to go with the flow or to modify your behavior, if the latter will present a better outcome for you and perhaps others.

2. Value others' points of view

Although you are entitled to your opinions and points of view, you will open up communication, break down walls of self-defense, and promote harmony if you listen to others with an open mind. Instead of clinging to your opinion, which may be a narrow point of view, be open to new ways of looking at things. Make it a habit to look for new facts and new ways to interpret facts; this habit will help you to deal more effectively with various situations that arise.

Instead of taking a position or jumping to a single conclusion or opinion, explore the facts, discuss options and alternatives, and look at different aspects of the situation. Many times, there is more than one valid point of view. In fact, there can be as many different points of view as there are people involved because each person's point of view is influenced by such things as the person's own particular interest, previous experiences, and his or her emotional state at the time. And although different, all the points of view may be valid.

I speak and train all over the country, and I have found that when we practice exercises during the sessions, participants are more inclined to use these simple techniques after they leave the program. And it is fun to share and listen to various participants' different points of view. We can't share verbally here, but let's take a situation that most of us can identify with and practice this exercise.

For instance, most of us have spent time waiting in the reception area of a busy dental office. For this practice scenario, the person has been waiting for quite a while past the time of the scheduled appointment. (The room may be called a reception area, but when we have to wait a while for our appointment, we think of it as a *waiting* room. Right?) For this exercise, look at the situation from the point of view of each of these three people and write your answer for each one.

• Person waiting for his or her appointment
   Point of view_____
• Receptionist
   Point of view_____
• Dentist
   Point of view_____

What point of view did you include for each? Was each point of view valid? Maybe you included more than one point of view for each. Because just as each will likely have a different point of view that may be valid, there is a wide range of possibilities for each person along a continuum.

Some of the points of view that you listed might include these:

• Point of view — Person waiting for his or her appointment

It is ridiculous to have to wait this long for an appointment I've had for six months. If they don't call me in the next two minutes, I'm leaving!*#*

• Point of view — Receptionist

I wish these people would quit asking me what's taking so long; I'm not the dentist; I just make the appointments. They should know that they'd have to wait!

• Point of view — Dentist

Wow! We're having a good day today. This means revenue will be up this month.

Would we agree that all of these were valid points of view? Perhaps we don't necessarily agree with some of their views, but we can see why they might think that way. Now let's look at some points of view on the other end of the continuum.

• Point of view — Person waiting for his or her appointment

I can see that they are really busy today. Maybe they had some emergency cases that got them behind. I'll check and see if it would be better for me to reschedule my appointment.

• Point of view — Receptionist

I know some of these people have busy schedules, and they should not have to wait so long. Let me see what I can do to expedite these appointments.

• Point of view — Dentist

We have several people waiting past their appointment times this morning and that's not good. We need to determine if over-scheduling caused this, but for now we need to let each one know approximately how much longer before we can get to him or her.

Again, each point of view is valid. And there are many other points of view that would fall along the continuum. And each person's standpoint would be valid for him or her.

I think that we would agree that the stress level would be different for each of these individuals depending on his or her point of view. Let's take the person waiting who was willing to look at the situation from the others' points of view. Realizing that emergencies or extenuating circumstances might have caused the delay would help this individual to stay in control.

In addition to making a difference in his or her personal stress level, the point of view taken could affect the stress level of those he/she comes in contact with. The people having to wait might feel additional stress from the receptionist who didn't seem to care that they had to wait.

Take time to look at others' points of view on a regular, routine basis. If you will seek to see the situation from the other's perspective so that you truly value his or her point of view, you will find this simple technique can be used in many situations to enhance your sense of well-being.

3. Be open to new possibilities

Listen carefully to information. Suspend judgment and refrain from expressing your opinion until you have listened attentively to key facts and ideas. Be willing to not only listen to new information but to think it over before adopting a position about it. Rather than focusing on the flaws of a new idea, examine an idea in terms of its merit by using the P.I.N. formula developed by Dr. Edward deBono. Using this simple technique forces one to find something both positive and interesting about the idea, yet still allows one to include a negative thought about the idea.

P.I.N. Formula

Positive Aspect of the Idea
Interesting Aspect
Negative Aspect

Develop the habit of using this formula in your dealings with people, and you just might find an idea actually has value. By being open to others' ideas, you will likely find that people share more with you, and you will be better informed. You still have the right to your opinions and decisions, but staying open to other possibilities can make you a much more effective problem-solver and innovator.

4. Control Worry

Some of us would probably say that we don't worry. Perhaps we would say that we feel troubled, anxious, or concerned. Whichever term we choose, from time to time, most of us worry to some degree and this can increase stress. To be flexible when dealing with stress, one can use a simple formula developed by Willis H. Carrier and promoted by Dale Carnegie. It is called the "Worry Formula." However, it can also be used very effectively when dealing with change, the unknown, and many of the other things that cause stress.

If something is causing you stress due to worry or concern, apply the magic formula by doing these three things:

1. Ask yourself, "What is the worst that can possibly happen?"
2. Prepare to accept it if you have to.
3. Then calmly proceed to improve on the worst.

When faced with an actual problem, no matter how extreme, typically we can deal with it. It is the unknown that usually gives us the most difficulty. By using this formula, we will be preparing for the unknown and usually will find that we can handle whatever we have determined to be the worst thing that can happen. Once we prepare to accept the worst that could happen, we will typically feel immediate relief from stress.

To give you a personal example, I found an opportunity to use this formula soon after beginning a new job teaching at a university. I liked to travel and with this new position, I had to plan trips so that they coincided with the university breaks. After diligently searching for a trip abroad that would fit within the fall semester break, I finally found a tour that just fit. Two faculty preparation days would precede the first day of classes, and the tour schedule allowed me to return home the day before the first preparation day. The okay was given for the trip, but the program director emphatically told me that I must be in the department for the first faculty preparation day with no exception. Well, of course, I expected to be back for the first preparation day.

Everything was going fine until the final day of the tour when we were to fly home. We were in Bali, Indonesia, and due to a political situation, all flights were cancelled; and not only were flights cancelled that day, they did not know when flights would go out. Remembering the director's words, I began to feel stress and to ponder the situation.

At this same time, my traveling partner became tickled and began to express her excitement. This upset me even more, and I told her that I didn't think this was anything to cheer about. To which she exclaimed that this meant we would have an extra day of vacation, and it would be a free day because the airline would be responsible.

I replied that this would cause me a serious problem at work. Then I realized that I was letting myself get upset about something over which I had absolutely no control. Rarely do I have to deal with a worry problem because I am on the low end of the scale when it comes to worry. So here I was just letting myself get caught up in the situation rather than deal with it effectively. But as soon as I caught myself, I went through the formula.

What I determined to be the worst thing that could happen was that I would be fired. At that time, my choice was to continue teaching at the university, yet I knew that I could get another job if necessary. So I prepared to accept being fired should it happen. Immediately I felt relief and knew that I could survive whatever happened. I might not like it but I could handle it. Since there really was nothing that I could do to change or modify the situation, I took advantage of this free day. I further relieved my stress by relaxing on the beach, getting a massage, and parasailing. (It was a fantastic day, and everything worked out fine!)

As in this example, it does not matter how simple or how quick and easy a procedure is, it does us no good unless we use it. Sometimes a technique looks so simple that we do not give it the merit that it deserves. Yet if we will go through the process, it will often help us to be flexible and deal more appropriately with stress.

5. Change or modify your behavior as needed

The words "as needed" are important to this characteristic, for you may not need to make changes in your behavior. This means that you will analyze the situation to determine if the outcome would be better if you made some changes and if so, to do so.

Make it a habit to scrutinize your mind-set, snap reactions, and automatic responses in situations to determine if they are appropriate. Many times we are not consciously aware of our thinking and reacting processes in these circumstances. If you see that what you are doing is not working well, try something else as you seek an optimum outcome.

Sometimes we are reluctant to change our behavior because of what others might think. However, when we make these changes, we usually gain rather than lose the respect of others. Most people recognize the willingness to change when needed as a trait of a good leader.

6. Take good care of yourself

If you want to be flexible, it is important that you take good care of yourself. When you take care of yourself on a regular basis, you feel better and thus find it easier to deal with everyday stressors. On the other hand, when you neglect taking care of yourself, you might find even small stressors too much to handle.

Taking care of yourself includes eating healthy, exercising, and getting enough sleep. It also requires spending time regularly doing things that give you pleasure. If you are not taking time for yourself, begin now.

Make a list of things that make you feel good, and be sure to include ones that you could do in a short period of time. Make it a practice each day to spend at least twenty minutes on yourself doing something that you enjoy. If your first impulse is to say that you cannot take twenty minutes daily for yourself, then begin with ten minutes or five or whatever you can squeeze in. If you will begin this daily practice, you will find the results rewarding enough that you will gradually add to the time allowed. And remember that it only takes doing something for 21 consecutive days to develop a habit, and this would be a good one to develop.

Two additional things that will make life better and help you to be flexible are to *look for the humor in everyday things* and *count your blessings*. If you look for the humor, you can find it. In some cases, it is harder to find than in others, but eventually you will discover the humor if you keep looking. And if you are looking for humor in ordinary times, you will have a much better chance to find it when the pressure is on.

As for blessings, everyone has things for which to be thankful. And if you make a practice of counting your blessings regularly, you will more fully realize just how much you have to be thankful about. Maybe you would like to make a daily gratuity list as many people over the country are now doing. At the end of each day, write five things that you are grateful for. If you do this, you will find that it causes you to focus more on positives. And it also helps you to pause and enjoy some of the little things that you might otherwise overlook— because these might be the only things for that day to put on your list. Regularly looking for the humor and counting your blessings will surely make you feel better and make it easier for you to deal with stressors.

Be flexible and control stress!

We have talked about six techniques that are common sense exercises anyone can use any time, any place to be flexible and control stress. If you do these things regularly and routinely, you will maintain balance and calm in your life; and then when you're faced with high stress, you'll be in a better state of mind to handle it. Be a good manager of your life, and you will benefit mentally, emotionally, spiritually, and physically. And when life gives you lemons, you will make lemonade.

Make it a great life!

ABOUT
JOLENE CARSON, R.T., M.A.

*J*olene Carson inspires people to take action. With over 20 years experience training and teaching, she draws from personal experience in presenting practical information that can be used immediately. And she's funny! She is a successful speaker, author, consultant and founder of SUCCESSabilities. She received a graduate degree in Human Relations and Supervision/Industrial Organizational Psychology from Louisiana Tech University and taught at the University of Louisiana-Monroe. She is also a registered Radiology Technologist.

Jolene likes inspiring people to "reach for the sky" at work and home. Her focus is in helping clients find new paths to success through communication, flexibility, cooperation and taking responsibility for personal accomplishment. She is a member of the National Speakers Association and worked as a Graduate Assistant with several Dale Carnegie classes.

Contact information:
Jolene Carson
SUCCESSabilities
P.O. Box 426
Hodge, LA 71247
Phone: (318) 395-8656
Fax: (318) 259-7385
Email: Jolene@JoleneCarson.com
Web: www.JoleneCarson.com

JEST FOR STRESS

by Karyn Buxman, R.N., M.S.N., CSP

In today's fast-paced society, we're all faced with some degree of stress: Cranky customers, irritable bosses, stubborn employees, budgets, deadlines, telephones, paperwork, a bad hair day, a no hair day. . . . For many of us, a straightjacket may be nearer than we think! It probably comes as no surprise that U.S. workers consume 15 tons of aspirin a day or that one in four workers suffers from an anxiety-related illness. Soon job stress may be the #1 reason for workers' compensation. "Terminal professionalism" seems to be a sign of the times. But taking oneself too seriously can have some nasty side effects.

What is Stress?

Stress is the body's response to any demand or pressure, and these demands are called stressors. A stressor might be a major life event, such as the death of a loved one or divorce. Stressors could entail chronic strains such as living in an abusive relationship. Stressors can also consist of occasional strains, like getting a flat tire in rush hour traffic.

Response to Stress

Stress requires our bodies to make adjustments physically, psychologically, socially, and even spiritually to maintain the necessary balance for survival. Too much stress (distress) can reveal itself in a number of ways. Maybe you recognize these signs in a co-worker or even in yourself:

Psychologically, when we are experiencing stress, we probably feel increased anxiety and tension. We may exhibit moodiness, irritability, inability to concentrate, crying, changes in eating patterns, changes in sleeping patterns, decreased sex drive, worrying, mood swings, frustration, nervousness, and depression. As if that wasn't enough, we may also demonstrate a negative attitude, low productivity, confusion, lack of creativity, lethargy, forgetfulness, or boredom. Have you ever had one of those days when you feel so frustrated that you just want to go home and kick the dog . . . and then you remember you don't even own a dog!

Socially, we may isolate ourselves from others, feel lonely, or make fewer contacts with friends. Communication may be hampered due to preoccupation with stressful events or hindered by negative mood swings, such as lashing out at others, nagging, or clamming up. We find ourselves thinking or saying, "Just leave me alone!"

Stress affects the physiology of all our major body systems. Breathing tends to be more rapid but shallow, not allowing for full air exchange deep in the lungs. The heart rate quickens and blood pressure increases. We may experience a feeling of the heart "racing" or "jumping out of the chest." The circulatory system shifts the blood supply from the surface of our bodies to muscles and major organs. Have you ever noticed your hands feeling cold, but you weren't in a cold environment? If you don't suffer from a vascular disease (such as Raynaud's), your hand temperature is often an excellent indicator of your stress level.

During stressful events, the immune system becomes depressed, resulting in an increased susceptibility to viral and bacterial infections. Cumulative stressful events can often lead to illness. For example, you get behind on a couple of projects and come down with a cold . . . a co-worker gets downsized and you inherit his clients and the next thing you know, you've got bronchitis . . . a virus deletes precious files on your hard drive and now you've developed walking pneumonia . . . then you're notified that your department is being audited and before you know it, you end up in the hospital on a ventilator!

During a stressful experience, muscles become tense, preparing for the "Fight or Flight" response. A person may notice headaches or a variety of muscle aches; clenched jaws or grinding teeth; tight neck, shoulder and back muscles and clenched fists. Have you ever found yourself gripping your steering wheel a little too tightly? (Hint: Your knuckles aren't typically blanched white . . .) Here's a quick tip: Note the position of your tongue. If it's resting in the bottom of your mouth, you're probably feeling relaxed. If it's pressed against the roof of your mouth, chances are you're experiencing some tension.

As for the digestive system, we may encounter a variety of symptoms ranging from cold sores around the mouth to nausea, vomiting, constipation, or diarrhea. There's nothing like numerous emergency trips to the bathroom to keep that cycle of stress building!

Nearly everyone recognizes the rising health care costs in this country. These costs put an escalating burden on employers as they cut into the corporate bottom line. Experts estimate that employee health costs consume nearly 50 percent of corporate profits. The good news: Humor is a cost effective and simple way to ward off many of the detrimental effects of stress.

What is Humor?

E. B. White once said, "Humor can be dissected, as a frog can, but the thing dies in the process and the innards are discouraging to any but the pure scientific mind." Many a scientist has attempted to define humor but few, if any, can agree on a definition. Be that as it may, I define humor as that which lends itself to laughing, smiling, or amusement. It's considered a positive emotion and may be used synonymously with a sense of joy. It has characteristics that make it a practical coping mechanism. That which appeals to one person's sense of humor may be offensive to others. Everyone's sense of humor is unique.

According to Dr. Vera Robinson, author of *Humor and the Health Professions*, humor has three functions: Psychological, social, and communicative.

Psychologically, humor acts as a major, healthy coping mechanism, relieving anxiety and tension. It serves as an outlet for hostility and anger, provides a healthy escape from reality, and lightens heaviness related to minor and major stressors. When employees must work on a job that is repetitive, humor can increase length of time on task by reducing tension and boredom. Studies also show that humor doesn't detract from tasks requiring increased concentration. Granted, things can sometimes get out of hand. Therefore, it's important to have a high performance norm and high expectations of the staff.

Socially, humor lessens the hierarchy between people, establishes rapport, and decreases the social gap. Humor solidifies a group. Victor Borge once said, "Laughter is the shortest distance between two people." Workers that can share a laugh develop a connection. Much office humor is "inside" humor or "you had to be there" humor. While this kind of humor can make folks feel like part of the gang, it can also make others feel excluded. Be careful that this humor is used constructively, and not to shut out others.

Over 80 percent of conflict results from problems with *communication*. Humor can help by gaining and holding the listener's attention. Humor can help establish rapport and neutralize emotionally charged interpersonal events. Humor opens the door for communication and conveys information by allowing one to bring up a secretly serious subject to see how it will be received while providing an 'out' such as "I was only joking."

There are also physiological effects related to humor and laughter. Think back to a time when you experienced a really good belly laugh. While you were laughing, you actually increased your respiratory activity and improved your oxygen exchange. During "belly laughter," air is inhaled deep into the lungs and exhaled forcefully. Smokers or those with a respiratory complaint, such as a cold or bronchitis, frequently experience coughing after laughter. This allows the body to further clear the airways and further facilitate the good air exchange.

In the cardiovascular system, laughter stimulates our heart rate and blood pressure. This increase is then followed by a relaxation phase, decreasing both heart rate and blood pressure. According to Dr. William Fry, a leading researcher in the field of psychoneuroimmunology, laughter provides an excellent cardiovascular workout. This exercise requires no special equipment and no limit to the number of times it can be used. Great news! You can get rid of those expensive sweater hangers (also known as treadmills, stationary bikes, stair steppers . . .). You can laugh at your desk, in the break room, in your car — just pick a spot and begin!

Scientists are making exciting discoveries regarding humor and the immune system. For example, studies reveal an increase in Immuno-globulin A, which fights upper respiratory tract infections. Additionally, there is an increase in the number and activity of natural killer cells, which attack viral infected cells and some types of cancer cells and tumors. An increase in activated T-cells (white blood cells) is seen, as well as an increase in gamma interferon and an increase in Immuno-globulin G and Complement C. Translated, this means that humor and laughter seem to be producing some very positive effects on our immune systems. They are not a replacement for traditional medicine, but can be considered a positive complement to medical treatment.

Other body systems also demonstrate changes during humor and laughter. Muscles briefly tense up but then relax, often resulting in diminished pain. In the sympathetic nervous system, catecholamine production increases, resulting in improved levels of alertness and memory and enhanced learning and creativity (and in these times when we're being asked to do more and more with less and less, who couldn't benefit from some increased creativity?). Stress hormones such as epinephrine and dopamine exhibit a measurable drop. Laughter stimulates both sides of the brain at the same time, coordinating all the senses and producing a unique level of consciousness and a high level of brain processing. Internal organs are massaged, so that laughter, like walking, can improve digestion. Tears of laughter (and crying) carry away toxins found in cells under stress. Any miracle drug that could do all this would cost a fortune!

Constructive and Destructive Humor

While nothing is black and white, humor can basically be categorized by that which is constructive and that which is destructive.

Constructive humor raises self-esteem, is supportive, includes people, reduces tension, confronts stereotypic ideas, breaks down barriers, relaxes people, stimulates new ideas, and creates energy and a positive atmosphere. Destructive humor lowers self-esteem, belittles others, excludes others, creates tension, perpetuates a stereotype, creates barriers, creates defensiveness, closes off creative thought, and focuses on negatives. In its most simplistic form, it boils down to laughing with someone versus laughing at someone. When promoting humor as a means of stress management, the emphasis should be on constructive humor.

Because everyone's sense of humor is highly individualized, we risk offending others when using humor. However, there are some basic guidelines to make humor a safer bet by remembering the acronym *B.E.T.*

Bond: The stronger your relationship and rapport is with the recipient of your humor, the more successful you'll be. How well do you know one another? Is there a mutual perception of the connection between the two of you?

It's been said that actor/comedian George Burns made a visit to a nursing home to entertain residents there. He walked up to a little old woman in her wheelchair, leaned toward her and teased, "Do you know who I am?"

The lady studied him for a moment and then answered cautiously, "No, but if you ask that nice nurse up at the front desk, I bet she could tell you."

If the recipients of your humor are busy trying to size up your relationship, the humor may go right over their head.

Environment: Anyone who sees your humor, hears your humor, or participates in your humor is part of your humor environment, regardless of whether or not that was your intention.

Dan manned his trade booth, ready to share information about the new product line, when lo and behold, his old college roommate, Roger, walked up front and center. They reminisced about the good old days and then started tossing one liners and jokes at each other. Dan was so busy telling

Roger the one about the brunette, the redhead, and the dumb blonde, that he didn't notice the association attendee patiently standing by, thumbing through the literature. Upon hearing his joke, she shook her head and moved on.

The humor you share may be just right for the intended 'audience,' but if it isn't appropriate for your entire 'audience,' save it for later.

Timing: There are two aspects of timing to keep in consideration. The first has to do with the manner in which you tell the humor. It's such a drag to listen to someone drone on and on, jump back and forth in the story, and then massacre the punch line. Some people are naturals at joke telling. For others, it's an acquired skill. If it doesn't come easily to you, practice your joke aloud, in front of a mirror, at least seven times. Then go out and share it at every appropriate opportunity. And if jokes aren't your bag, no problem. We all have an abundant resource of funny stories that happened to us, a co-worker, a friend, a family member, etc. (Tip: A great source for potentially funny stories are your most embarrassing moments.) Practice telling the story out loud, and cut out any parts that aren't crucial. As Shakespeare wisely said, "Brevity is the soul of wit."

The other aspect of timing has to do with the relationship of the humor to an event. Most, if not all, humor comes from pain or discomfort, whether it's yours or someone else's. If it's someone else's, a certain amount of time needs to elapse before he or she sees the humor in the situation. It gets a little tricky, as the amount of time required for each person varies. When in doubt, let the other person signal the 'all clear.'

Mary returned to the meeting in the conference room after the break and resumed her place at the front of the room, standing by the flip chart. It was several moments before she realized, that when using the ladies room, she had tucked her skirt into the back of her panty hose. Red-faced, she excused herself from the room and pulled herself back together. Not a word was mentioned, until after lunch when Mary looked at the people seated around the table and said, "You know, Mom was right. It's always important to wear clean underwear. You

just never know when you're gonna be in an accident!"
Everyone burst out laughing and began sharing his own most
embarrassing moment.

Taking Action

Set the tone: If you're in a position of leadership, give the staff permission to have fun. "Walk your talk." Be willing to overcome the fear
of foolishness. Don't be afraid to look a little silly: a goofy hat, tie,
button, socks, etc.

I once presented a program to middle and upper management at a Chicago hospital. The response was tremendous: "This is just what our employees need!" They brought
me back six weeks later to address the entire hospital staff. A
comment that showed up on numerous evaluations surprised
me: "This was wonderful. I just wish my boss could have
heard the message." How sad. Their bosses felt that humor
was reason enough to bring me back so I could share the
message with the staff but not important enough to demonstrate themselves.

Set the environment: Humorous posters, memos, and signs can
lighten the surroundings. Bulletin boards displaying cartoons, jokes, and
funny notes don't take a big investment but can provide an abundance
of entertainment. Create a positive working atmosphere at the desks
with toys such as Legos, Nerf guns, Silly Putty, Koosh balls and hula-
hoops. Add some comic activities or theme days to the calendar.
Encourage everyone to be involved: Administration and management,
all departments, customers or patients, volunteers and family members.
A "M.A.S.H." day when everyone dresses up like the characters on the
television show by the same name, or a western theme when everyone
dons cowboy boots and bandannas can lighten the atmosphere for staff
and clients or customers. A little competition between floors or departments might increase interest.

At BizLand.com, every employee receives a monthly

"fun budget" of $15 for toys for the office. The office now has remote control cars, a mini-lacrosse set, inflatable furniture, and Nerf toys of all kinds. Marketing manager Tricia O'Neil purchased the lacrosse set and explains, "Our hallways at (work) make a perfect playing field. I can teach others the basics of lacrosse, have a little break, and improve my agility with a little pick-up game." (Bowling, anyone?)

Set the pace: If you agree that humor in the workplace is a valuable idea, don't delay taking action. Too often, humor and fun are seen as frivolous and unimportant.

Lee Iacocca understands the need for both work and play. He says, "Over the years, many executives have said to me with pride, 'Boy, I worked so hard last year that I didn't take any vacation.'"

"I always feel like responding, 'You dummy. You mean to tell me that you can take responsibility for an $80 million project and you can't plan two weeks out of the year to have some fun?!'"

No one suggests that you attempt to be a stand-up comic or laugh constantly. It is important, however, to attempt to use humor routinely. Whatever forms of humor you choose, it's important to practice them on a regular basis. When humor happens by accident, there are positive benefits. There are too many rewards, however, to let humor happen strictly by chance. Don't let stress come between you and the realization of your goals. Put your stress in check by making humor a habit — jest for stress!

Getting Started

Studies confirm that you gain many more benefits by being an active participant in humor rather than a passive observer. Here are some ideas that will put humor to work for you!

- Make a list of things that are fun *for you* and do one item daily
- See a movie of your choice (via theater or video, but popcorn either way)

- Have a marshmallow fight (you can eat the leftover ammunition)
- Participate in a massage train (if you make a circle, no one gets left out)
- Take a joke break (these can be programmed into your computer)
- Practice standing ovations for yourself and co-workers
- Read something for enjoyment
- Write a silly limerick
- Send a humorous card (earn bonus points if for no special occasion)
- Leave a humorous message on your own answering machine
- Keep a humor file at your desk and refer to it daily
- Wear a funny button or pin
- Lighten up your work environment (cartoons/props/photos/toys/etc.)
- Can the Muzak for something fun and upbeat
- Plan a theme day (dress down day/wild west/beach day/etc.)
- Eat fun food (Snickers bars, Ho Hos, Cracker Jacks, etc.)
- Try your hand at juggling (scarves are the easiest to learn)
- Sing silly songs
- Buy your very own humorous prop, like a magic wand or goofy glasses
- Share your most embarrassing moment
- Start your day with 20 seconds of laughter (fake it till you make it)
- Hold a cartoon caption contest
- Have a good laugh — at yourself
- Read more humor tips (subscribe-lytebytes@humorx.com)

Side Bar: ©2001, Karyn Buxman, RN, MSN, CSP

Functions of Humor

Psychological: Acts as a major coping mechanism; relieves anxiety and tension, serves as outlet for hostility and anger, provides healthy escape from reality, and lightens heaviness related to critical illness, trauma, disfigurement, and death.

Social: Lessens the hierarchy between individuals, establishes rapport, and decreases social distance.

Communicative: Helps convey information; opens the door for communication by allowing one to bring up a secretly serious subject to see how it will be received while providing an 'out' such as "I was only joking."

Physiology of Laughter

Respiratory System: Increases respiratory activity and oxygen exchange.

Cardiovascular System: Stimulates heart rate and blood pressure followed by a relaxation phase; vasodilatation.

Sympathetic Nervous System: Increases production of catecholamines resulting in increased levels of alertness and memory; enhances learning and creativity.

Immune System: Immunoglobulin A found in significantly increased levels of saliva with stimulation of humor and laughter, increased spontaneous lymphocyte blastogenesis, a natural killer cell activity.

Muscle System: Stimulates muscles and relaxes muscle tension, often resulting in diminished pain.

Brain: Laughter stimulates both hemispheres at the same time, coordinating all the senses and producing a unique level of consciousness and a high level of brain processing.

Digestive Tract: Internal organs massaged resulting in increased peristalsis, improved digestion.

Tears (of laughter and grief): Provides exocrine response, carrying away toxins found in cells under stress.

ABOUT
KARYN BUXMAN, R.N., M.S.N, CSP

A highly sought humorist and internationally recognized expert in therapeutic humor, Karyn Buxman shows people how to manage their stress and improve their bottom line through humor and laughter. Karyn realized it was time to leave bedside nursing when, as she watched a movie starring Mel Gibson, caught herself staring longingly — at his large veins. She switched to a career in speaking when she realized it didn't have to be done in 12-hour shifts, didn't involve body fluids, and didn't require white support pantyhose.

Karyn is an active member of the American Association for Therapeutic Humor, International Society of Humor Studies, National Speakers Association, co-founder of The World Laughter Tour, author of This Won't Hurt a Bit!, *and publisher of a quarterly newsletter,* Wits & Bits. *Her hobbies include making beds, folding laundry, washing dishes, vacuuming, and scrubbing toilets. (Would you like to buy a bridge?)*

Contact information:
Karyn Buxman
HUMORx
P.O. Box 1273
Hannibal, MO 63401-1273
Phone: (573) 221-9086
Fax: (573) 221-7226
E-mail: Karyn@HUMORx.com
Website: www.HUMORx.com

Resource Listing

Karyn Buxman
HUMORx
P.O. Box 1273
Hannibal, MO 63401-1273
Phone: (573) 221-9086
Fax: (573) 221-7226
E-mail: Karyn@HUMORx.com
Website: wwwHUMORx.com

Jolene Carson
SUCCESSabilities
P.O. Box 426
Hodge, LA 71247
Phone: (318) 395-8656
Fax: (318) 259-7385
Email: Jolene@JoleneCarson.com
Website: www.JoleneCarson.com

Suzie Dawson
Chrysalis Coaching
12315 Jones Maltsberger #406
San Antonio, TX 78247
Phone: (210) 402-5424
E-mail: suziedawson@earthlink.net
Website: www.Chrysalis-Coaching.com

Bonnie Dean
W.O.W. Presentations
11823 Purslane Circle
Fountain Valley, CA 92708
Phone: (714) 531-7035
Phone: 800 915-4668
Fax: (714) 531-1903
E-mail: bon4motion@aol.com
Website: www.BonnieDean.com

Jane Sullivan-Durand, M.D.
Center for Integrative Medicine
171 Pleasant Street
Concord, NH 03301
Phone: (603) 228-7600
Fax:: (603) 228-7320
E-mail: DrJane@DrJane.com
Website: www.DrJane.com

Gerry Grinold
1423 W. Kinsel Highway
Charlotte, MI 48813
Phone: (517) 543-7004
Fax: (517) 543-2099
E-mail:grinold@voyager.net

Nancy Hedrick
ReGen Enterprises, LLC
12811 West 131st Street
Overland Park, KS 66213
Phone: (913) 814-9504
Fax: (913) 685-7413
E-mail: nchedrick@aol.com
Website: www.ReGen-Ent.com

Mark Hunter
MJH & Associates
15633 Underwood
Omaha, NE 68118
Phone: (402) 445-2110
Fax: (402) 445-0942
E mail: MarkJHunter@email.msn.com

Celeste Jonson
celeste jonson International, Inc.
200 North Pickett Street
Suite 1405
Alexandria, VA 22304
Phone: (703) 461- 7955
Fax: (703) 461-7966
E-mail: jonsoninc@aol.com
Website: www.celestejonson.com

Deborah Kern, Ph.D.
605 County Road 1184
Cullman, AL 35057
Phone: (256) 775-3716
Fax: (413) 751-5109
E-mail:Dr.Deb@DeborahKern.com
Website: www.DeborahKern.com

Natalie Manor
Natalie Manor Associates
P.O. Box 1508
Merrimack, NH 03054
Phone: (800) 666-2230
Fax: (603) 424-1267
E-mail:
CoachNatalie@manorevents.mv.com
Website:
www.NatalieManorAssociates.com

Jamie Montelongo
Touchstone Massage Therapy
4118 McCullough Avenue
Suite 7
San Antonio, TX 78212
Phone: (210) 822-2848
Fax: (210) 494-3882
Email: JMontelongo@juno.com

Caterina Rando
182 22nd Avenue
San Francisco, CA 94121
Phone: (415) 668-4535
Phone: (800) 966-3603
Fax: (415) 668-6450
E-mail: CPR@CaterinaR.com
Website: www.CaterinaR.com

Laurie Richards
Laurie Richards & Associates
12 Purple Martin
Hackettstown, NJ 07840
Phone: (908) 813-3971
Email: ladrichard@aol.com

Paul Schnabel
Schnabel Impact Group, Inc.
10875 N. 118th Way
Scottsdale, AZ 85259
Phone: (480) 767-8965
Fax: (480) 767-3578
E-mail: Paul@PaulSchnabel.com
Website: www.paulschnabel.com

Stephen Siemens, CSP
Siemens People Builders
6478 NE 5th Avenue
Des Moines, IA 50317-9102
Phone: (888) SAY STEVE
Phone: (515) 265-8748
Fax: (515) 265-5750
Email steve@ThePeopleBuilder.com
Website: www.ThePeopleBuilder.com

Holly Stiel
Holly Speaks
728 Bay Road
Mill Valley, CA 94941
Phone: (415) 383-4220
Fax: (415) 383-1503
E-mail: HollySpeaks@aol.com
www.ThankYouVeryMuchInc.com

Dr. Patricia Tice
The Tea Doctor
4861 Park Drive
West Des Moines, IA 50265-5330
Phone: (515) 457-7590
E-mail: pktice@home.com
Website: www.theteadoctor.com

Dr. Karen Wolfe
P.O. Box 3833
Mission Viejo, CA 92690
Phone/Fax: (949) 581-3269
E-mail: Info@DrKarenWolfe.com
Website: www.DrKarenWolfe.com

Anja and Frank Wynne
Marlboro Road 9
41176 Moenchengladbach
Germany
E-mail: WynneGrp@aol.com
Wesite: www.WynneGroup.com